The HUMAN BODY

WHAT IT IS AND HOW IT WORKS

TEXT BY MITCHELL WILSON

ILLUSTRATIONS BY CORNELIUS DE WITT

ARTHUR W. SELIGMANN, M.D., MEDICAL CONSULTANT

GOLDEN PRESS NEW YORK

Western Publishing Company, Inc.

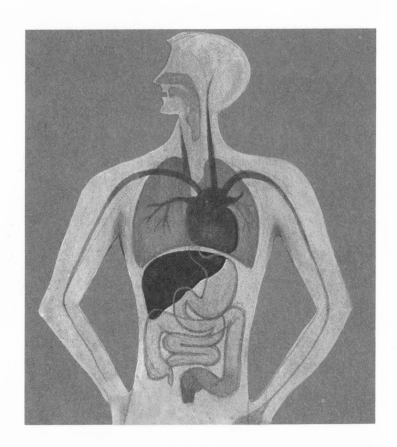

ACKNOWLEDGMENTS

The publishers gratefully acknowledge the cooperation of Alfred A. Knopf, Inc. in making available Fritz Kahn's *Man in Structure and Function* (1943), on which the idea and conception of many of the illustrations are based.

The artist also extends his sincere thanks to the following for their advice and assistance in preparing the illustrations for this book:

Dr. M. Diesnis of Nice, France
Prof. Ovidio Lefebvre d'Ovidio of Rome, Italy, and São Paulo, Brazil
Dr. I. Knittel of Paris, France
Dr. Arthur Seligmann of New York City

Twelfth Printing, 1972

Library of Congress Catalog Card Number: 59-16889

Contents

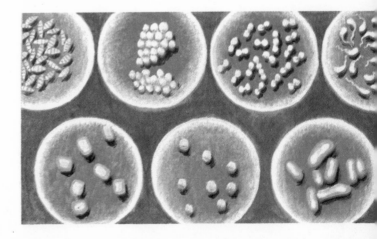

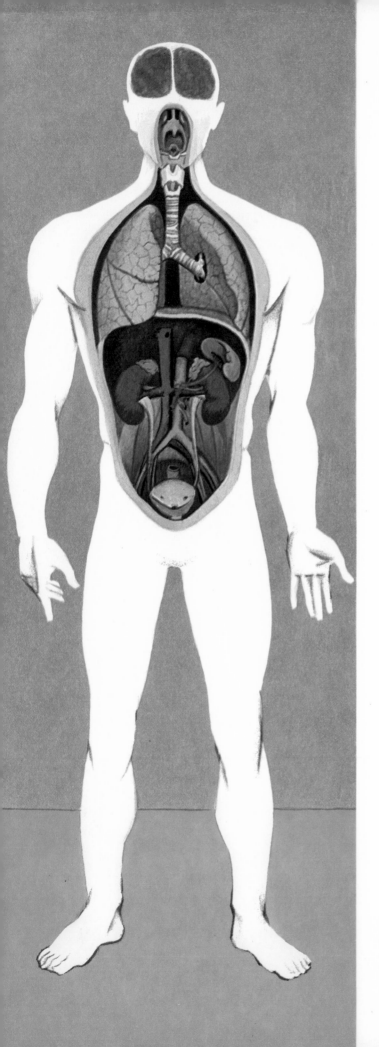

Introduction

Aᴌᴍᴏsᴛ ɴᴏᴛʜɪɴɢ, it seems, could be more important to man than the human body. It is the solid part of "I"; it is with us as long as we live. Yet thousands and thousands of years passed before man really learned much about this physical part of himself.

Among the ancients, health was something given by the gods. If you had an accident or got sick, it was because you had displeased the gods, or a demon had entered your body. The demon had to be eliminated, the gods made happy, before you could get well. Breathing and digestion, the circulation of the blood, the working of the brain—these functions that keep a human being alive and active were not understood. The few real facts that were known were badly mixed up with superstition.

The first ancient thinker to fight free from superstition was a Greek of the fifth century ʙ.ᴄ.: Hippocrates. Much like a modern scientist, he observed the human body carefully, wrote down what he saw, and drew his conclusions from his observations, without regard to demons and such. His work was as much a declaration of independence as the one written about in history books.

But men like Hippocrates are few. After the great age of Greece, scientific observation and thinking became rare. For nearly two thousand years, new ideas and the questioning of old ideas were discouraged. Testing and experimenting were not proper for men of learning. Scholars concentrated on problems of religion, and they inherited their ideas from the past.

At the close of the Middle Ages, however, the world was changing. Artists and scholars were again becoming interested in the thinkers of ancient Greece and Rome. Merchants were traveling more widely—as far as India and China. Thoughtful people were becoming restless—impatient with old ideas, ready for new ones. Columbus and his voyages were just one sign of the times.

It was just about fifty years after Columbus discovered America that an Italian thinker, Vesalius, discovered the human body. Vesalius was one of those people who were taking a fresh, inquiring look at the world—asking questions of the kind that mean scientific progress. Vesalius went much further than Hippocrates in making observations and setting up standards of study for others to follow. When he had the opportunity, he performed dissections to learn about the inside of the body. Fine drawings of the body made by an artist under his direction made a great impression, and thousands of people learned from them.

It is hard to believe that most of the facts of human anatomy known today by high-school students were unknown only four hundred years ago. We have come a long way since then. True, the road of learning has been hard and slow, and any doctor will be quick to say that much is still unknown. But everyone today can have a clear understanding of the more important parts of the body and how they work.

Why is that important? The body is probably the greatest scientific wonder of the world, and so it is the perfect subject with which to begin the study of science. Knowledge of the body helps us to keep healthy and to understand what the doctor tells us when we are sick. And for any young person planning to become a doctor or a nurse, the study of the body is a first step.

The story of the human body really has no ending. Tomorrow a chemist or a biologist may discover a new fact about the body that will make a new chapter in our knowledge—or even a new book. But let these pages be your beginning. They can start you on the way toward a growing understanding of the human body and its ways.

M.W.

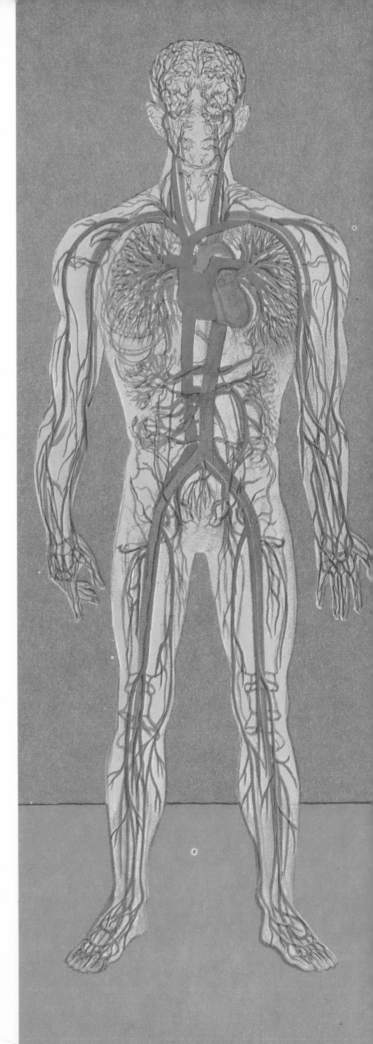

The Wonder of Life

A GREAT ruler once called his wise man to him and said: "I should like people to say that I bestow the greatest gifts in the world. What is the most wonderful thing a man can have?" The wise man answered: "The greatest gift in the world is not yours to give. Every living man already possesses the most valuable thing in the world—life. Nothing in the world, nothing in the universe, can

A drop of water seen under a microscope is a miniature world filled with simple forms of life.

would show itself thronged with forms of life so tiny that a hundred thousand of these miniature beings would make a line less than an inch long.

In that scene by the pond, though, the most wonderful form of life has yet to be described— you, the human being. No other form of life is as marvelous as the human body. No other form of life is as complex, nor can any do so many things. Every part of the body is alive, and virtually every part works to keep the whole body alive. A single book, even if it were ten times the length of this one, could not tell the full fascinating story of how this is done.

Life is so mysterious that even though everybody knows how it feels to be alive, no one has

compare in beauty or wonder with this, the most priceless of all gifts."

One of the wonderful things about life is its many forms. On a summer day stand by the side of a country pond. The green grass beneath your feet is alive. The tree that shades you with its leaves and branches is alive. The birds that sing above you are alive. The water teems with life: not only with animals but also with aquatic plants. Each drop of water held beneath a microscope

ever been able to explain what life really is. The most learned scientist can only describe some of the things that can be found in all forms of life— great and small.

Mysterious though life may be, we are slowly getting closer to understanding it. We are approaching the day when life will no longer be a mystery. New discoveries in chemistry, the invention of the electron microscope, the use of radioactive elements in biological research—all

Many different kinds of fish, plants, bacteria, and insect larvae live together in a pond. The various forms feed upon and support each other.

these have been of great help to the scientist. With such tools as these, man is slowly learning the structure of the simpler forms of life. Once he has learned to understand this structure, the next step will be the actual creation of life in the laboratory—and even this is no longer the wild idea it seemed half a century ago when man had not yet harnessed atomic energy or heard of jet airplanes. However, at present the goal of creating life is but the dream of the biologist. There have been times when man has come close, but he has yet to be successful in probing life's secrets. For the present, all he can do is describe life in all its various forms and show how every living thing is related to every other, how they all have certain things in common.

Any living thing feeds itself and must have food to stay alive. Some animals eat leaves, berries, or grass; others need meat. Trees and other living plants take in food through roots in the ground. It is often said that people need food in the same way that an automobile needs gasoline. Food is said to be "fuel." This is true, but only partly true, for of course automobiles are not alive.

All species of living things are able to create offspring almost in their own likeness. The tiny creatures of the water that can be seen only through a microscope create new tiny creatures like themselves. Trees drop seeds that root in the ground and grow to become new trees. Hens have baby chicks. Human beings give birth to children.

All this is called reproduction. It is something that only living things can do. And it is one test of what we call life. Man may never be able to create anything so wonderful and complex as he himself is, but the creation of even the tiniest form of life, if it is able to reproduce itself, will be a major discovery—perhaps the most important discovery that man has ever made.

Only living creatures, then, can feed and reproduce—and these are the two most important things that living creatures do. Even the smallest, simplest form of life feeds and reproduces. This simplest form of life is a one-celled organism, and simple

13

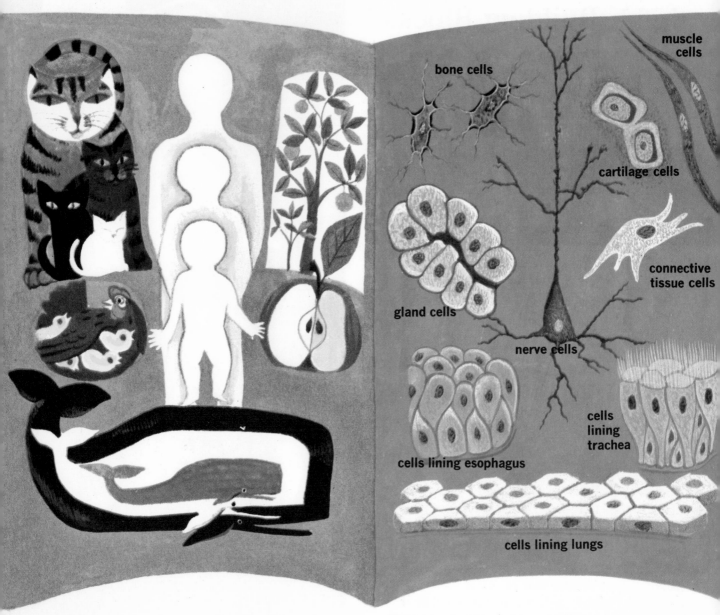

bone cells

muscle cells

cartilage cells

connective tissue cells

gland cells

nerve cells

cells lining trachea

cells lining esophagus

cells lining lungs

Only living things can reproduce out of themselves new living things almost exactly like themselves.

The human body is made up of billions of single cells, of which there are many different kinds.

though it may be, this is the form that man is so eager to create in the laboratory.

Like all complicated creatures, the human being is actually made up of billions of single cells, of which there are many kinds. Groups of single cells cluster by the millions to form the special parts of the body.

One kind of cell clusters in layers or sheets to make up the skin. A second kind clusters to form the type of muscle with which we can make the various parts of the body move. A third kind of cell forms another sort of muscle that can perform movements without any conscious control by the mind; a fourth kind forms the nerves that make up the body's communication system. There are at least a half-dozen different types of cells that make up the blood. Still others take care of the body's other needs. The full list could fill pages.

The final human being is, of course, very different from any of the single cells that help make him up. There is no single-celled creature in the world that can laugh, sing, dance, read, know what joy feels like, or how it is to be sad, or the fun of learning something new.

Human beings have truly been given the priceless gift of life in its most marvelous form.

Life's Building Blocks

THE CELL is the smallest unit of life. Life began many millions of years ago in the sea, and probably as a result of this origin, the cell is made up largely of liquid. The cell can be thought of as a very tiny globe with a liquid center and a thin, protective cover—called a membrane—enclosing it. The entire life of the cell is regulated by the membrane. All the nourishment the cell receives filters into it through the membrane, and the cell's waste products filter out through it. If the membrane is damaged or destroyed, the cell dies.

The membrane encloses the cell's fluid, and in this fluid is suspended a still smaller droplet which is enclosed by another membrane. Like the meat inside a nut, this is the most important part of the cell and is called the nucleus, from the Latin word for the kernel, or inside part, of a nut. The nucleus itself could be called a cell except that it cannot live without the cell fluid around it. In the nucleus lie all the materials that are used by the cell to reproduce itself. Digestion of food takes place in the cell fluid, and there also the cell stores up extra food that it will use at a later time.

Different kinds of cells do special jobs. Gland cells produce and give out special juices that the body needs. For example, the cells of the sweat glands secrete a fluid that no other kind of cell can make. Muscle cells are so formed that they can tighten and relax, and so move the various parts of the body. Nerve cells are the only cells in the body that can pass along messages from the parts of the body to the brain or spinal cord.

The cells are life's building blocks. Just as bridges, houses, and machines are all made up of small, simple parts, so all living things—from the one-celled amoeba to the human body—are made up of cells.

Even the simplest organisms feed and reproduce. The hydra (right) waves food into its mouth with tentacles. The amoeba (below) surrounds its food.

AMOEBA TAKING IN FOOD

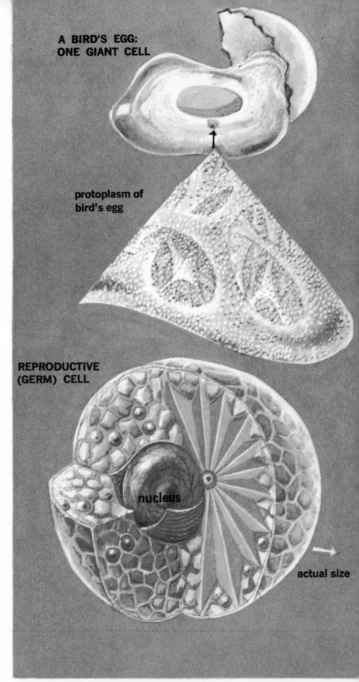

A BIRD'S EGG: ONE GIANT CELL

protoplasm of bird's egg

REPRODUCTIVE (GERM) CELL

nucleus

actual size

food

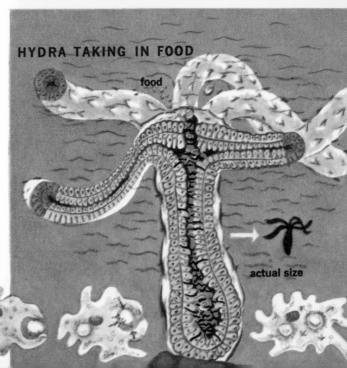

HYDRA TAKING IN FOOD

food

actual size

How Cells Join Together

Wʜᴇɴ a large number of the same kind of cells are found together, they are said to form tissue. In the body there are six kinds of tissue.

The first kind is covering tissue. Examples of this are the skin and the covering of the inside of the mouth, and the digestive organs.

A second kind is connective tissue. It binds muscles together, forms the capsules around joints, anchors organs in place, and forms a loose supporting network under the skin. The blood is a third kind of tissue. Muscle tissue is the fourth, nervous tissue the fifth, and glandular tissue the sixth.

Nervous tissue is different from all the others because it is the only kind of tissue that cannot heal itself by growing new nerve cells. Damaged skin, for example, is healed when the skin cells reproduce and create new skin cells to take the place of those that were destroyed. The same is true of muscle cells. Bone tissue can heal, and even blood renews itself.

A group of different tissues working together to do a special job forms a mass called an organ. An eye is an organ, as are the brain, the heart, the liver, and many other parts of the body.

A group of organs working together to do a complicated job for sustaining the life of the body is called a system. For example, the mouth, the stomach, and the intestines are organs that work together for the handling of food. They make up part of the digestive system.

Just as cells form tissues, tissues form organs, and organs form systems. All of the systems together form the human body. How all these systems work together so efficiently, each one helping to sustain the body, is a great mystery of life.

Just as houses are made up of bricks, boards, tiles, pipes, and fittings; so the human body is composed of single cells forming tissues, blood vessels, bones, organs, and complete systems.

cell

tissue

organ

system

The Nine Systems

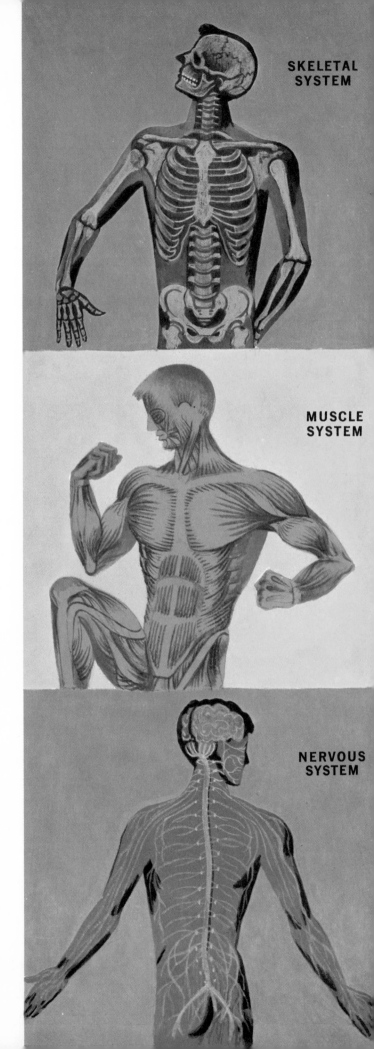

SKELETAL SYSTEM

MUSCLE SYSTEM

NERVOUS SYSTEM

THE OPEN highway stretches out before your family car, twisting and turning through the countryside, and there is never a moment's doubt that the car will follow every curve in the road to take you where you want to go. What makes it possible for the car to do this? You might say, "The steering wheel." But that is not the full answer by any means. Making a car turn the way you want, when you want, is a complicated job requiring a large number of parts. Together, these parts form the "steering system." An automobile needs many such systems to make it go.

Like an automobile, the human body needs many systems to allow it to function. In general, it is possible to group the organs of the body into nine major systems.

1. To begin with, just as every building has some kind of framework to support it, so has the human body. Instead of beams and steel girders, the framework of the human body consists of 206 bones. The SKELETAL SYSTEM includes not only the bones, but the connective tissues that hold them together. One of the very important differences between the framework of a house and the human body is that parts of the body must be able to move. Bones are not attached rigidly, but are connected by joints that allow movement.

2. Bones can move only when they are pulled. Tough tissue in the form of sheets and ropes, called muscles, does this work. Man has over 600 muscles in the MUSCLE SYSTEM. This system not only moves arms, legs, feet, hands, fingers, the head, and the trunk of the body, but also has the job of pushing food through the body and making the blood circulate through the heart. Wherever there is movement in the body the muscles do the work. The eye muscles, for instance, move your eyes to read these lines.

3. Muscles do not move bones by chance. A muscle moves a bone when it is signaled to do so by the brain. The brain decided to make

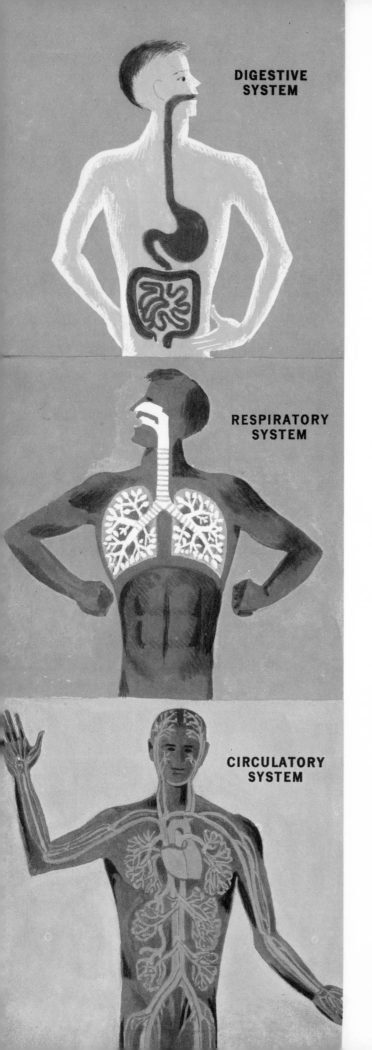

DIGESTIVE SYSTEM

RESPIRATORY SYSTEM

CIRCULATORY SYSTEM

a particular movement because it has received a signal that calls for such a movement. It is as if the body were equipped with a combined radio-television-telephone network. We call it the NERVOUS SYSTEM. Nerves in the skin that react to heat and cold are part of this system. The eyes use part of the system when they send messages to the brain describing what is seen. The ears, the nose, and the tongue use the system to send messages describing what is heard, smelled, and tasted. It is your nervous system that tells you what you are reading at this very moment.

4. Movement of the body means that the body is working and therefore using energy. This energy is replaced by energy we get from food. The DIGESTIVE SYSTEM is the name of the group of organs that break up food so that it can be absorbed to supply energy for living and working. Not all foods give the same amount of energy— beefsteak offers more than celery, for example— but the digestive organs can handle all kinds of food and extract the best values from them.

You found the energy to pick up this book, the energy to read it, and the energy to understand what you read—three very different forms of work—because of your digestive system.

5. For the body to use the energy it gets from food, a substance called oxygen is needed. Oxygen is an invisible gas that is present in the air around us, but it is mixed with other gases which the body does not need. Oxygen must be separated from the rest of the gases. The body has a special system which includes the nose, the throat, the windpipe, the bronchial tubes, and the lungs—the RESPIRATORY SYSTEM—to deliver air into the body from which it extracts oxygen. Taking air into the body is called inhaling. The body does this automatically. When the body is working so hard that a great deal of energy is needed, more oxygen than usual is taken in. That is why we breathe fast when we have been running or jumping. The respiratory system also extracts carbon dioxide and exhales it from the body.

6. The energy-producing substances taken from the food by the digestive system and the oxygen separated from the air by the respira-

tory system have to be circulated through the body as rapidly and thoroughly as possible. Blood is the fluid that does the job. The CIRCULATORY SYSTEM, consisting of tubes of tissue called veins and arteries, directs the blood to all parts of the body. The blood moves through the arteries, passes through tubes called capillaries, then goes into the veins. It flows through the circulatory system because it is pumped by an organ of muscle called the heart and by muscles in the blood vessels.

7. Even though the blood vessels branch out to all parts of the body, the food that is circulated does not pass directly from the blood to the individual cells. A colorless fluid called lymph is squeezed out of the tiniest blood vessels, and it is the lymph that bathes the individual cells of tissue and supplies them with food. Lymph surrounds the cells in the same way that air surrounds the entire human being. The LYMPHATIC SYSTEM consists of the lymph fluid, the lymph vessels—which return the lymph to the veins and arteries—and the lymph glands. Lymph glands purify the lymph fluid.

8. The different systems are themselves controlled by the nervous system, as well as by another system which sees to it that they all work at the proper rate. Substances known as hormones circulate through the body by means of the bloodstream. These hormones act as messengers to the different systems, regulating their activities to satisfy the body's needs from moment to moment. The ENDOCRINE SYSTEM produces these hormones from the endocrine glands. For example, when we are angry, hormones give us the sudden burst of strength needed to put up a good fight.

9. As the body goes about its work of living, cells and tissues wear out and are continually replaced by new cells. This repair work is possible because many cells can reproduce themselves. Reproduction of this kind goes on all the time in the body. However, the body is also able to reproduce a completely new living creature almost exactly like itself. This is what happens when parents have a child. The body has a separate group of organs, the REPRODUCTIVE SYSTEM, that provides for this—the most miraculous act of life.

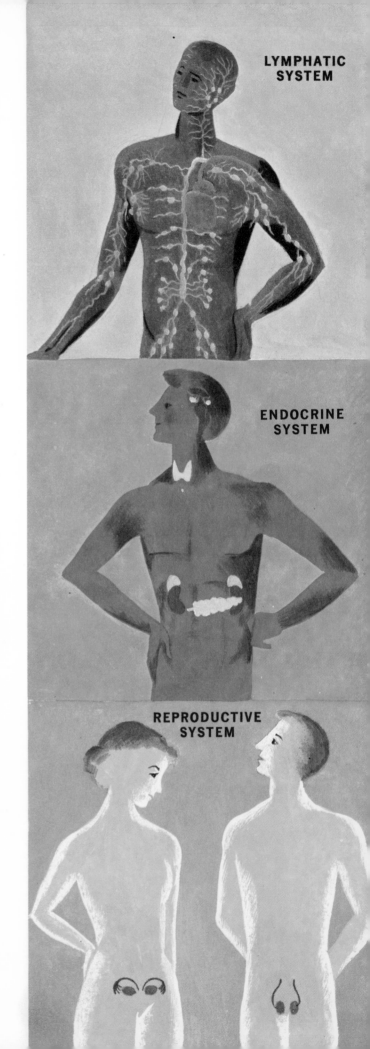

LYMPHATIC SYSTEM

ENDOCRINE SYSTEM

REPRODUCTIVE SYSTEM

The Miracle of Skin

Fingerprints are used for identification, since those of no two people in the world are the same.

IF YOU LIKE riddles, ask yourself this question: which part of the body grows faster than any other part and never stops growing, even though it never gets any bigger once it has reached its full size? The answer is the human skin.

The outer layer of the skin has a name that goes back to ancient Greek days: *epidermis*, which means "outer skin." The epidermis is a form of protective armor. Single cells are fluid and must live in fluid. But because the body must live in air, there is need for a covering to contain the body's fluids. This covering is really several layers of dead skin cells stretched out and flattened.

Every day, these layers of skin are rubbed off and replaced by the layer underneath. All during the body's lifetime, the under layer of the skin continually creates new cells. This is one of the reasons why a cut on, for example, the finger heals over very quickly. Even a scrape or bruise that covers a fairly large area heals in a short time.

Underneath the outer layer is a much deeper one called the dermis. It is in the dermis that most of the marvelous powers of the skin come into play. For example, if the outer skin is to stay supple and strong, it must be constantly oiled. Oil glands in the skin, connected with the hair roots, do this job.

Each hair has a root that goes down into the dermis through a special shaft. This shaft is called a hair follicle. Each follicle is connected to a gland, the sebaceous gland, which pours an oily liquid into it. The liquid runs up along the hair follicle and reaches the outer surface of the skin. Some people's hair is more oily than others because their sebaceous glands are more active.

The skin not only keeps itself oiled; it also helps to keep the temperature of the body steady. This is done by means of the sweat glands. These little sacs, deep in the dermis, produce a fluid that by evaporation helps to control body temperature. By means of a twisting tube, each gland's fluid reaches the outer skin through an opening called a pore. When the body is hot, from hard work or sunshine, the pores open up and sweat flows out over the skin. The water in the sweat evaporates and reduces the skin heat. When the body is cold, the pores close up and no sweat reaches the skin.

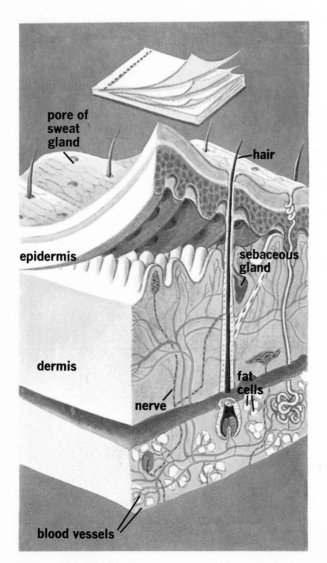

pore of sweat gland

hair

epidermis

sebaceous gland

dermis

nerve

fat cells

blood vessels

The human skin is formed of layers, like a pad of notepaper. Blood vessels and nerves run through it.

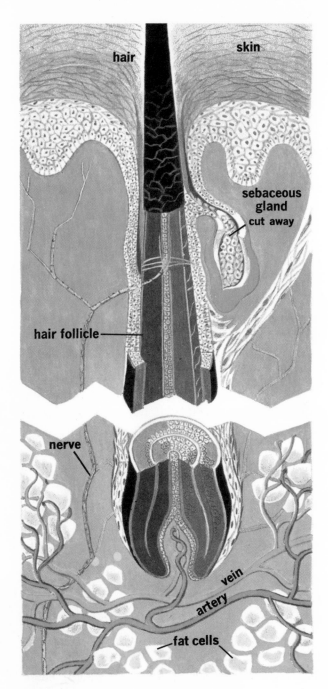

Special creams help protect the skin's surface in strong sunlight, and keep it from being burned.

mostly on the color of his parents' skin. It also depends on the amount of sunlight the person gets and on substances called hormones.

Sunlight makes these special cells more active and in this way may cause the skin to turn brown. Sometimes only small areas are affected, and when this happens, a person is said to be freckled.

The skin is the frontier between the body and the outer world. Imbedded in its surface are a large number of tiny organs called sense organs, which are connected to nerve endings. These sense organs and nerve endings warn us away from things that are too hot or too cold, and enable us to have a sense of touch. They detect sensations in the world around us and transmit impulses to the brain where the sensations are identified. Because of its sense organs, the body can recognize dangerous sensations and act to avoid injury. Just as the cell's membrane protects the cell, the skin protects the body.

Daily baths and scrubbing remove the dirt, salt, and dead skin that form on the skin's surface.

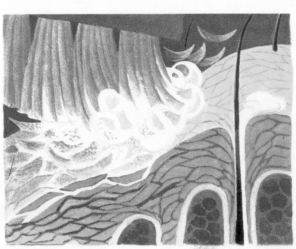

Cutaway view of hair showing hair follicle, blood vessels, nerves, and sebaceous gland.

As sweat evaporates, it leaves behind salts and other solids on the skin. There are also accumulations of flakes of dead skin, oil from the sebaceous glands, and dirt. Warm baths wash away these materials. Baths also leave the skin glowing, and the body refreshed.

There are cells of still another type in the skin, which determine the skin's color. They manufacture a substance called melanin, a dark pigment. The amount of it in the skin of a person depends

Bones—Framework of the Body

BENEATH the magic walls of the human skin, cushioned by varying amounts of fat and a loose network of supporting tissue, lies the great power-house of the muscles. But before discussing them, it is important to know what some of the muscles move: the bones, which are the very framework of the human body.

No part of the body has just one job. The skin heals itself, oils itself, and heats and cools the body. In the same way, the bones have a great number of things to do at the same time. They are not at all as simple as they look.

The 206 bones of the human body may be roughly divided into two kinds. Touch your head, your shoulder blades, and your hips. These are flat bones. The second kind includes those we

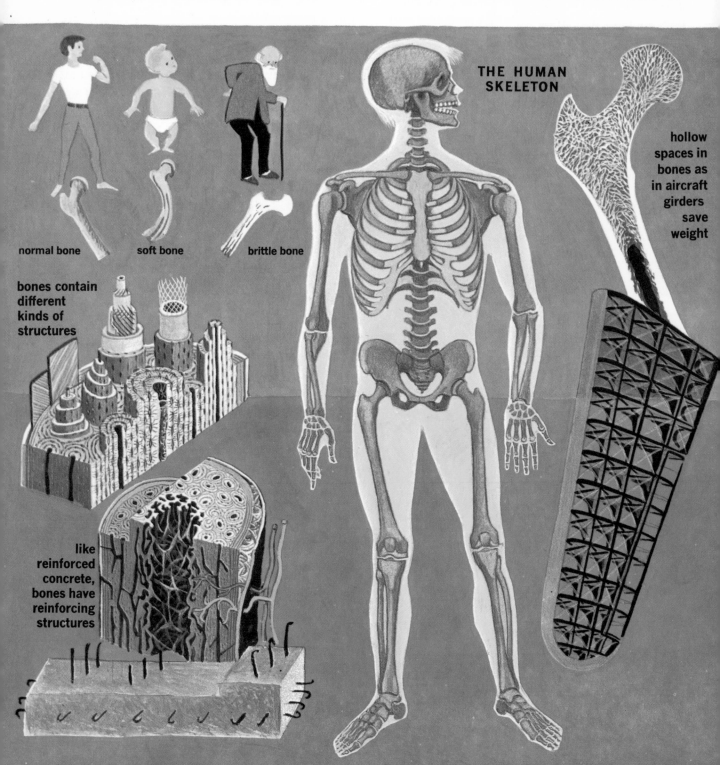

normal bone   soft bone   brittle bone

THE HUMAN SKELETON

hollow spaces in bones as in aircraft girders save weight

bones contain different kinds of structures

like reinforced concrete, bones have reinforcing structures

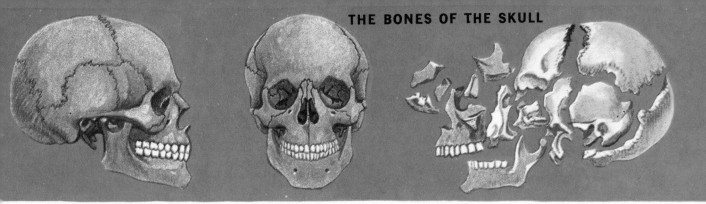

Although the human skull seems to be one simple surface, it is actually made up of a large number of smooth bones. These bones are joined together to make a perfect natural dome which is very strong.

have in our arms and legs: long bones. All living bone supports and gives shape to a particular part of the body. Bones can also act as rich storehouses for some of the most important chemicals the body needs; and the flat bones are busy factories where many of the cells of the bloodstream are made.

It took man thousands of years to learn some of the concepts of building that had been used all along in his own body. Although we think of the dome as one of man's great building achievements, the bones of the head—the cranium—have long formed a perfect natural dome.

Tall buildings, airplanes, and ocean liners are supported by a framework of girders. It was very long ago that men found out that even hollow girders can be very strong; but the human body was made according to this plan from the very beginning, for most bones are hollow. Inside them is a soft tissue called marrow, which in the flat bones manufactures both the red and white cells of the blood.

The marrow lies inside the hard, white, spongy case, the cortex, which most people think of as

ARCHITECTURE AND THE HUMAN FRAME

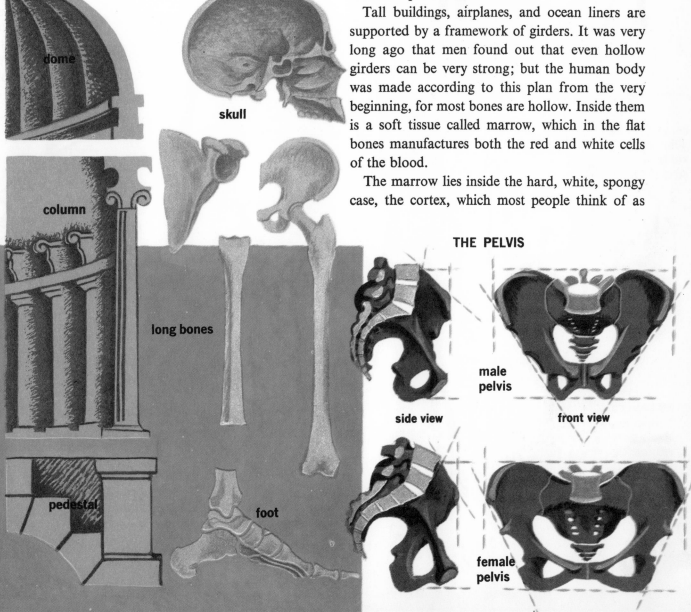

dome

skull

column

long bones

pedestal

foot

THE PELVIS

male pelvis

side view

front view

female pelvis

A bone may break in several different ways. But no matter how it breaks, the healing process is always the same. 1. Types of bone breaks and healed fracture (lower right) with bulge of callus sealing break. 2. Blood clots in and around break. 3. New bone cells enter the break. 4. The bone hardens and (5) is finally healed.

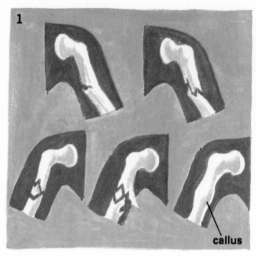
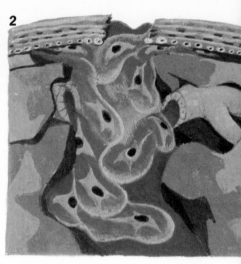

callus

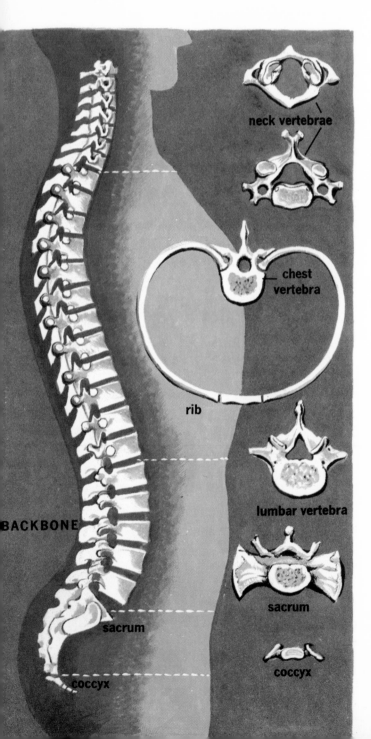

neck vertebrae

chest vertebra

rib

lumbar vertebra

sacrum

coccyx

BACKBONE

sacrum

coccyx

the bone. But even though this case looks and feels solid, it has many tiny openings for blood vessels to pass in and out bringing nourishment. Larger blood-vessels also pass through the bone case, going to and from the marrow.

Two different substances, calcium and phosphorus, make up most of the cortex. Calcium makes the bone white and hard. Phosphorus is used in the nucleus of all cells, but particularly in nerve and bone cells. Whole milk is a good source of calcium and phosphorus. This is why growing persons need about a quart of milk a day.

In order for it to stay alive, the body is in constant need of calcium and phosphorus; and the bones give them off as needed. If, for one reason or another, the balance of calcium and phosphorus in the body is disturbed, the bones become too brittle or too hard.

Children all over the world used to suffer from a bone disease called rickets. But the discovery of vitamins showed how this disease could be cured. Doctors found that when a certain chemical called vitamin D is present, children do not develop rickets. The body makes vitamin D when the sun's rays shine on bare skin. For extra safety against rickets, vitamin D is now often added to milk or provided in special oils. Today everyone knows how important milk and sunshine are in building strong and healthy teeth and bones.

The backbone is made up of separate blocks. These blocks, called vertebrae, are fitted together to provide a flexible yet strong support for the body.

3
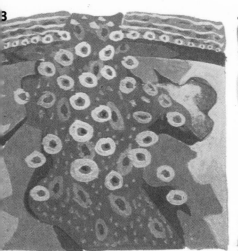

4
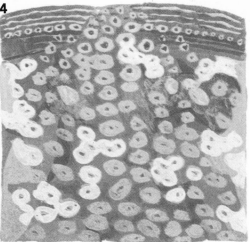

5
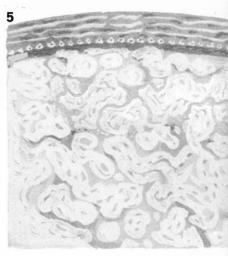

Hands and feet are so cleverly made that they will be discussed separately. No machine ever made by man is quite as remarkably built as the human hand.

The main support of the body—the backbone— is flexible, yet powerfully strong. Run your finger up and down your spine. The little ridges tell you that the spinal column is made up of separate blocks. What you feel when you do this are little spiny projections attached to the main part of each block. The blocks are called vertebrae. Each one is fitted to the one beneath; but it is also separated from it by pads which soften the shock of movement. In the neck alone there are seven vertebrae. Twelve more vertebrae support the twelve ribs, and five very strong ones support the small of the back. In all, there are thirty-three.

In adults, the twenty-four upper vertebrae are often referred to as the "true" or "movable" verte-brae. The nine lower ones are called the "false" or "fixed" vertebrae. This is because the upper ones stay separate and flexible, while the lower ones usually unite to form two bones: the five in the small of the back forming the sacrum, the four beneath the sacrum forming the coccyx. The coccyx gets its name from the Greek word for cuckoo. It is said that an early anatomist thought he saw a resemblance between these bottom four vertebrae and the bill of a cuckoo.

The most sensitive part of any bone is the thin membrane that covers it. This sheet of tissue contains many fine blood vessels and nerves. Bones will not heal if this covering is badly damaged.

One of the miracles of nature is the way broken bones seem to know just how to heal themselves. When a bone is broken and the two edges are brought together, the affected area is surrounded by clotted blood and the watery substance called lymph. Each edge begins to make new cells and to push them out toward the other end of the break. No one yet knows how the bone is able to throw out these strands in the right direction, or why the bone continues to do this until the break is entirely healed, at which time the process stops.

In time, enough calcium is deposited around the broken ends to form a thick swelling of bone, healing the break entirely. This swelling is known as a callus. After it has healed, the bone becomes even stronger than it was before it was broken!

The building of this bridge of bone seems to start of its own accord. Just as mysteriously, the body brings it to an end.

But even though bones can heal by themselves, they usually can be made to heal better and straighter with some help from the outside. To support the broken ends of the bone, and to keep them in the proper position while they are healing, doctors usually put a cast around the break. This is done by wrapping a moistened bandage containing a powdery plaster around the broken arm or leg. This is carefully molded so that it fits exactly. Thus when the plaster hardens, it forms a strong case that holds the break in exactly the right position while the healing process seals over the jagged edges. The limb soon becomes healthy again, and able to do everything it could before.

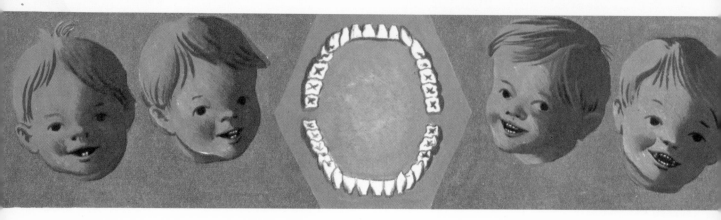

Teeth and Their Care

Teeth are really a kind of bone and should be considered part of the skeleton, even though they do not have the healing ability that bone has. Fortunately, teeth are covered by the hardest material in the entire human body—enamel. This covering is so hard that teeth can take great shocks without harm. Yet enamel is one of the few tissues that cannot repair damage to itself.

Every tooth has a soft center which contains nerves and blood vessels, and every tooth is rooted in the jaw. Human beings have two sets of teeth—a set that grows in early childhood, and a much tougher, larger set that grows in and pushes out the first set. The first set number twenty, and are called milk teeth. The second set of thirty-two—the jaw is now large enough to hold more teeth—is called the permanent set. But teeth will be permanent only if they are permanently cared for.

The upper and lower four teeth in front of each jaw have sharp cutting edges for biting food. They are called by the Latin word *incisor*, meaning "cutter."

On either side of the incisors, both upper and lower, is a sharp-pointed tooth that looks some-

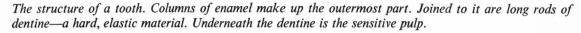
The structure of a tooth. Columns of enamel make up the outermost part. Joined to it are long rods of dentine—a hard, elastic material. Underneath the dentine is the sensitive pulp.

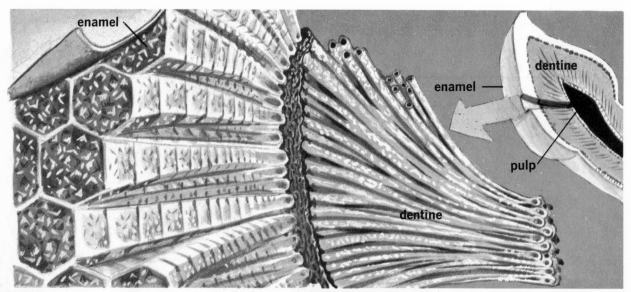

what like a dog's tooth and for that reason is called a canine tooth. There are four altogether. These teeth begin to be replaced in about the sixth year by a tougher set.

In the first set are eight teeth toward the back of the mouth for grinding food. These are called molars. Later, when the second or permanent teeth come in, we have a total of twelve new molars, along with eight other teeth between the molars and canines. These additional teeth are called bicuspids.

The working part of the tooth, as far as eating is concerned, is the crown. Generally, the crown is covered with an invisible layer of certain cells, called bacteria, which attack sugar. Pure sugar is turned into acid, which in turn dissolves enamel in spots. This dissolving of the enamel is the beginning of decay.

Decay usually begins in those places on the tooth where tiny particles of food are likely to be left behind after chewing. This is why it is good to brush teeth right after eating.

Tooth decay takes place most readily between the ages of five to eight and twelve to eighteen, when the body grows most rapidly.

When a spot of decay eats sufficiently through the enamel and the ivory under it, exposing the nerves of the pulp cavity to hot and cold or chemical substances such as acid and sugar, intense pain is felt. This is toothache. The spot is actually a hole that gets deeper, and becomes filled with particles of trapped food and bacteria.

The dentist can recognize a cavity because it appears as a dark brown spot on the tooth and feels soft when he places a pointed instrument in it. He uses a tiny drill to cut away the walls of the cavity, in which there is a deposit of decayed matter. He also uses the drill to give the hole the right shape to hold a filling.

The material used for filling teeth is soft and pliable when the dentist first mixes it. Within a very short time, however, the filling begins to harden and become solid.

Dentists use many types of material in filling teeth. Such materials range from simple "gutta

Cavities form when food particles lodge between the teeth, and bacteria work their way down to the inner part of the tooth. If a cavity becomes deep enough to reach the sensitive pulp, the result is toothache.

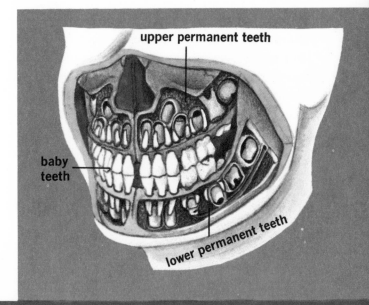

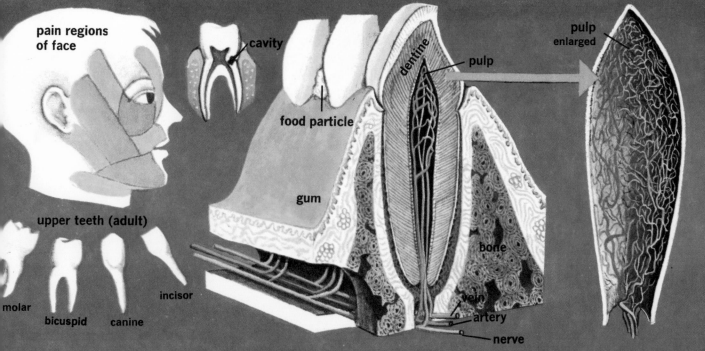

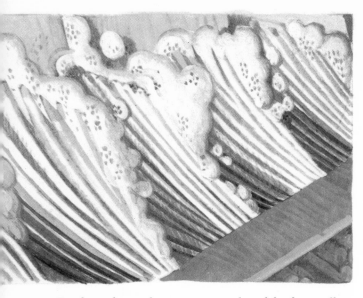

Brushing the teeth removes particles of food as well as harmful bacteria that may be present.

percha," which fills the cavity temporarily while the regular filling is being prepared, to gold and silver and porcelain. Sometimes the dentist must make a model of the cavity before he fills it. He does this by having his patient bite hard on a piece of soft wax. The wax becomes a mold of the tooth, complete with cavity. The mold is filled with wet plaster, which hardens into an exact model of the original tooth. The dentist then fills the space made by the cavity with molten gold. When the gold hardens, it is the exact shape to fill the cavity. Once inserted into the tooth this filling is called an inlay.

Sometimes the dentist will fix wire braces on teeth that are crooked. As the jawbone grows, the teeth slowly move into line with the help of the braces. This permits the person to chew properly and improves his speech and appearance.

Although dentists do a wonderful job filling cavities and saving teeth, it would be much better if cavities could be prevented altogether. This may soon be possible. Dental scientists have found that cavities develop much less often in the teeth of children living in certain areas. They discovered that this resistance to decay is related to the presence in the water supply of a chemical called fluorine, which seems to increase the absorption of calcium and phosphorus into the teeth.

To test the relationship between fluorine and tooth decay, scientists added a little of the chemical to the drinking water of a certain city for a period of several years. Then dentists examined the teeth of the children of the city and compared them with the teeth of children from another city where the water had not been treated. The children who had drunk treated water had far fewer cavities. As a result of the experiment, a number of cities have started adding fluorine to their water supply in small doses. Care must be taken, for too much causes mottling and discoloration of the teeth.

Calcium and phosphorus, as represented in diagram by cement, are constantly supplied to the teeth. They reinforce and strengthen them. The stronger the teeth, the better they resist harmful bacteria.

How Bones Are Joined

THE BALLET dancer turned slowly and gracefully on her toes; her arms lifted in a lovely gesture. In the spellbound audience, people thought, "How beautifully she moves!" At the end, they applauded and walked out of the theatre, not realizing that as they walked along, their own movements were as intricate as the dancer's.

The thousands of movements that the body can make are possible only because of the way the ends of bones are connected with their neighbors. These connections are called joints.

Turn your head slowly from side to side, or shake it up and down. You will see that the movement involves the joints of your neck. Raise your arm over your head and bring it straight down in front. All the movement takes place within the end of your shoulder. Raise your forearm, and you will see that the movement takes place within the elbow. All of these points are where one bone meets another; and for each movement, there is a different type of joint.

There are three principal kinds of joints. In the first, there can be no movement at all. The skull, for instance, is made up of flat bones that are closely fitted together. When a child is very young, these bones can be moved, but not of the child's own accord. The skull bones are equipped with edges that are jagged, like the teeth of a saw. As the years pass, these jagged edges fit together, and fibers that toughen with time hold them in place. The skull finally appears to be one solid mass of bone.

In the second type of joint, only a very slight movement is allowed. As you sit, turn your body from side to side. The movement is taking place all along the spine, each vertebra moving slightly. The spine is called a limited-movement joint because it allows a certain amount of flexibility, but not much. It is prevented from moving too easily by thick bands of strong, fiberlike tissue.

The third kind of joint includes the highly movable joints of the arms, legs, hands, and fingers. There are different types of these movable joints. One is like a hinge. Bend your knee or curl up your fingers, and you will see an example of the hinge joint in action. Another type of highly movable joint works like a pivot. Twist your forearm and see how the joint at the elbow works. If the lower part of the arm did not pivot like this, it would be far more difficult for you to turn a doorknob or take a cork out of a bottle.

Another movable joint allows for a circular motion that is not really rotation. For example, move your thumb around. The joint that permits this motion is called a saddle joint; it is between the thumb and the bone of the hand.

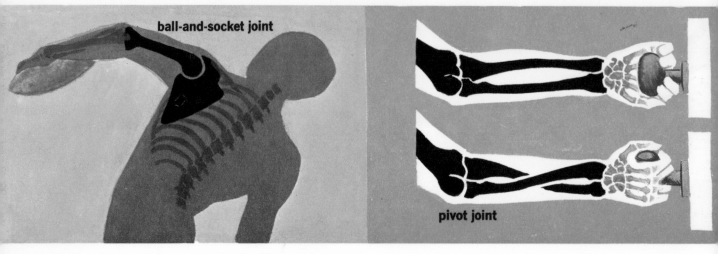

ball-and-socket joint

pivot joint

Ball-and-socket joints, as in the shoulder and hip, are among the most highly movable joints in the body.

The elbow's pivot joint makes it possible for the forearm to twist, as it does in turning a doorknob.

The most movable of all joints are in the hips and shoulders. You can swing your arms around almost in a wheel. Dancers can do much the same thing with their legs by swinging them from the hips. This kind of joint is called a ball-and-socket joint. To realize how important it is, watch a baseball game. The ball-and-socket joint of his shoulder allows the pitcher to throw the ball either overhand or sidearm. The range of movements made by a fielder—from reaching up over his head for a fly ball to scooping up a grounder—is made possible again by the joint of his shoulder. Another athlete who depends heavily upon the ball-and-socket joint of his shoulder in order to perform his specialty is the discus thrower in a track meet.

Joints such as these exist nowhere in nature except in living bodies; but man was so ingenious an engineer that he worked them out for himself in building, long before he knew about them in himself.

All joints in buildings have to be oiled. Otherwise door hinges, for instance, would become rusty and squeak, and then bind. Joints in the body also need oiling, but the oiling system is built into the body, into the very joint itself.

The ends of the bones are so shaped that they slide easily over each other. The ends of bones are faced with cartilage, which is smoother than bone. The cartilage lies underneath the membrane of the joint. Cartilage is the semi-hard substance

we call gristle when we encounter it in a roast chicken or turkey.

There are also membranes that give out a special fluid which fills the joint space. When something goes wrong with these membranes, and the joint is dry, movement can be very painful.

Near some of the joints are sacs called bursae, which are also lined with smooth membranes filled with fluid. They act as cushions between the ends of the bones and the muscles over them. Bursae are present around the knees, elbows, shoulders, and hips. Sometimes they become inflamed and extremely painful, and it is difficult to move the joint. This condition is called bursitis. It is fairly common, but not terribly serious.

Joints would not stay in position or last long if their parts were not lashed together to hold them steady. The ligaments take care of this. Ligaments are tough, fibrous sheets of tissue that surround the joints. Sometimes they form strips that connect the various parts of the joint. They steady the joint and allow it to move only the way that it is supposed to. In a "turned" ankle, it is the ligaments that hurt. What actually happens is that the ligaments tear while trying to keep the ankle in proper position when it is twisted. Then the ankle swells and sometimes turns black and blue. This means a few days of hobbling about, but the ligaments soon return to normal.

When a joint is strained to the point where the ends of the two bones that form it are separated,

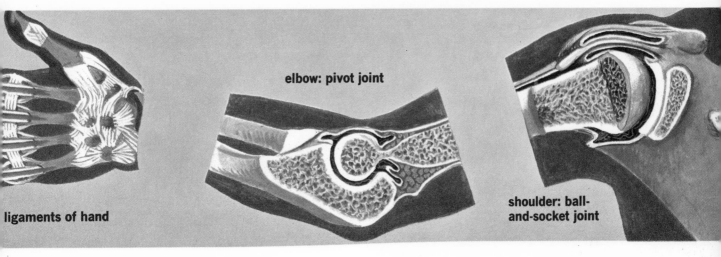

elbow: pivot joint

ligaments of hand

shoulder: ball-and-socket joint

There are two different kinds of ligaments. Some are strips of tissue that hold joints together. Others form thin sheets that cover the joint to protect it and keep it in position.

we say that the joint is dislocated. Dislocations of the shoulder are sometimes caused by trying to use the arms as a brace when falling suddenly; or a finger can become dislocated when a baseball hits the tip of it instead of going into the middle of the baseball glove.

Sometimes the bones go back into place of their own accord. If they don't, the doctor can get them back so that the joint can move comfortably again. Occasionally the lower jaw becomes dislocated after a very hard yawn and must be pushed back into place. Other joints are even less likely to become dislocated. The hip and the knee, for example, are far more sturdily constructed than are most of the joints of the body, and so only rarely become dislocated. Dislocations generally aren't serious and they heal quite rapidly.

Men long ago invented one type of movement for machinery that does not occur anywhere in the human body. This movement is pure rotation. There is no part of the body that can whirl around like a wheel.

But this does not mean that man is smarter than nature. After all, it was nature in the first place that created man with a mind clever enough to think of these things.

The different kinds of ligaments are shown in the picture below. In the spine, the ligament forms a protective covering. Tough strips in the knee and in the hip join the different parts of the joints.

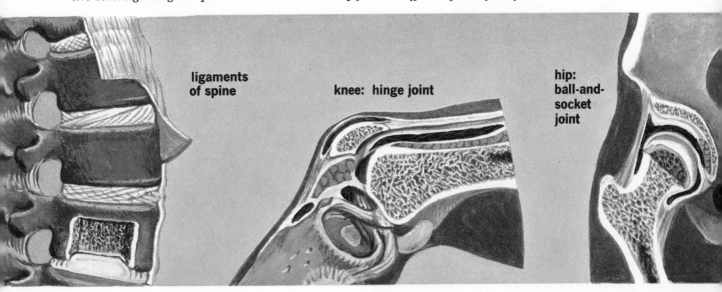

ligaments of spine

knee: hinge joint

hip: ball-and-socket joint

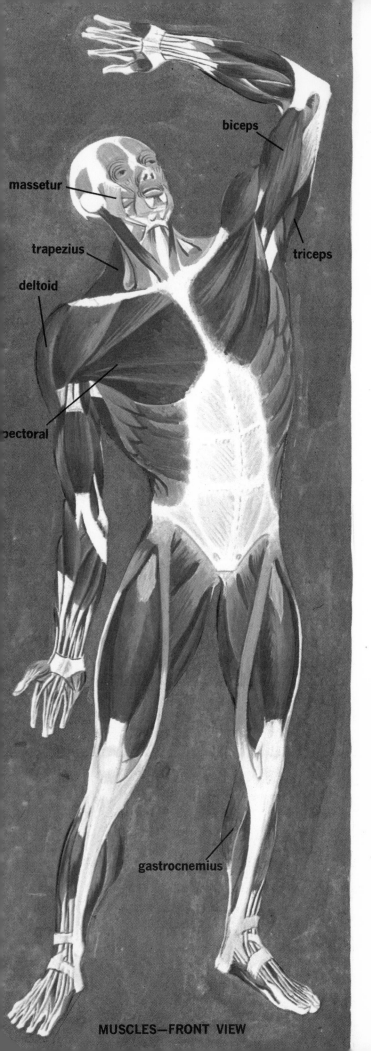

biceps

massetur

trapezius

deltoid

triceps

pectoral

gastrocnemius

MUSCLES—FRONT VIEW

Muscles—
Source of Strength

I<small>T IS IN</small> the joints of the body that movements of the bones take place. The movement itself is caused by the pull of sheets and cords of very tough tissue called muscle. Muscle tissue has the special ability to shorten itself so that the bone on which it pulls has to move. When muscle tissue shortens, it also bunches up.

"Make a muscle!" you say to a small boy. He knows very little about the human body, yet he knows enough to bring his forearm up so that his clenched fist gets as near as possible to his shoulder. The flesh on the front part of his upper arm bunches into a hard lump. This lump is the shortening of that particular arm muscle, the biceps.

Muscle tissue covers the body in sheets and bands that lie between the skin and the skeleton. The bones are the framework of the body, but it is the muscles that fill out the body shape. Most muscles extend from one bone to another. Suppose two bones are connected by muscle and one of the bones is held still. When the muscle between them shortens, the other bone has to move.

The point where the muscle is fastened to the unmoving bone is called the origin of the muscle. The point where the muscle is fastened to the bone that is to be moved is called the insertion.

Sometimes the muscle is not attached directly to the bone, but to a tough, non-stretchable cord, or tendon, which is attached to the bone.

To find out where a tendon is, put your hand on the thick portion of tissue at the rear part of your leg, just below the knee. This is one of the most powerful muscle groups in the body. As you move your hand down toward your ankle, the leg gets narrower. This is because the muscle does not extend all the way. Halfway down it is attached to a tendon, which extends all the way to the heel, called the Achilles tendon.

A few muscles have special functions. The diaphragm, for example, forces the lungs to take in air. This part of breathing is not primarily a bone-moving operation.

Muscles do not push; they can only pull. To bend the arm at the elbow, the muscle at the front of the upper arm has to shorten and bunch up. To unbend the arm, other muscles in the back of the arm have to shorten.

These two sets of muscles—the front and the back—are said to act in opposition to each other. When one set is working, the other set is usually relaxed. But there are times when both of them work. Bend your arm only halfway and then use your other hand to try to force it either up or down. To keep the arm bent, you must use both sets of muscles.

Sometimes muscles are called upon to do more than simply pull in one direction. They may have to perform a turning motion. To be able to do this, the muscle must be attached to the bone at an angle. By pulling, it can cause the bone to pivot.

Some muscles are attached to bones in several places. For example, the muscle at the front of the upper arm, the biceps, has two points of attachment at the shoulder. "Bi," which means two, refers to these two points. The rear muscle which extends from the upper arm to the forearm has three points of attachment at the shoulder. This muscle is called the triceps, since "tri" means three.

Most movements of the body require the action of more than one muscle. Even to bend the arm, the biceps has to work with two other muscles.

You can feel some of the most important muscles work. Put your fingertips over the center of your abdomen, and harden the muscle underneath. The muscle can be felt as a broad belt running up to the lower part of the ribs and extending down to where the legs join the body. The two rectus muscles make up this belt.

Put your hand on the top, outer part of your left arm just below the shoulder. Let your left arm swing easily back and forth and you will feel the deltoid muscle ripple beneath your fingers. You can feel this muscle bunch up when you swing your arm straight out from the side.

The muscles that we can control are called voluntary muscles. They are made up of particular types of cells which are long and look striped. The cells form long fibers of tissue, and the fibers are enclosed in a sheath. The muscles are covered with broad membranes.

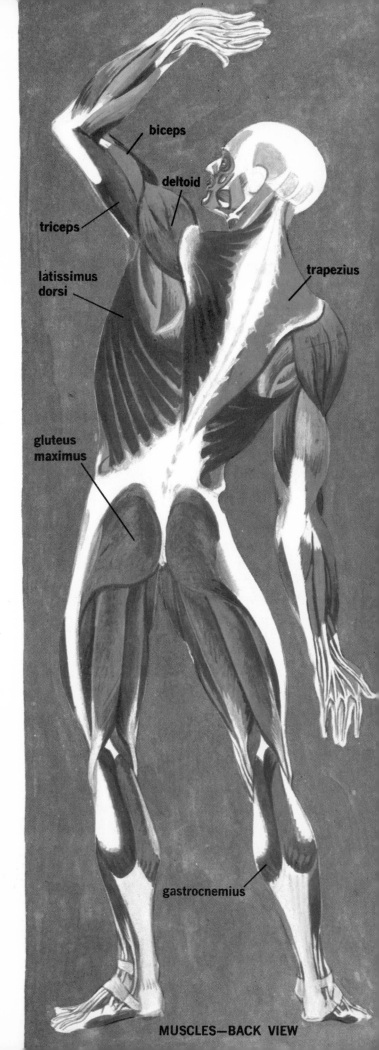

biceps
deltoid
triceps
latissimus dorsi
trapezius
gluteus maximus
gastrocnemius

MUSCLES—BACK VIEW

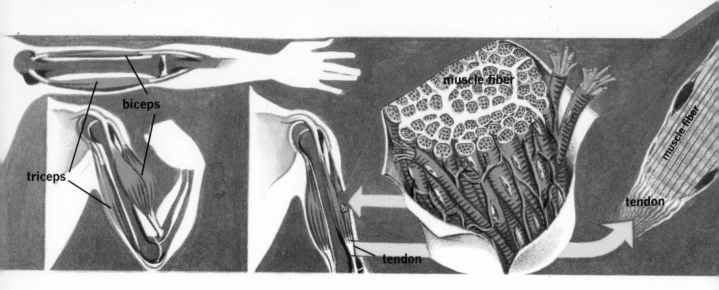

All the striped muscles of the body are made up of clusters of fibers of muscle tissue. The fibers are enclosed in individual sheaths and each muscle is itself covered by a protective membrane.

Not all the muscles of the body are under voluntary control. There are also smooth muscles, so-called because they are not striped like the muscles that we are able to control. Smooth muscle is found in the body organs and blood vessels. It narrows and widens the arteries, and pushes food through the stomach and intestines. In general, it does all the automatic moving jobs in the body. The exception is the muscle of the heart, which works automatically but looks more like the striped muscles. Smooth muscles function even when we are asleep or unconscious.

The size of the muscles in a person's body depends to a large extent on how much these

muscles are used. Baseball players and ballet dancers have bulging calf muscles. Boxers have bunchy arm muscles, and their calf muscles, too, are well developed.

No one gives all his muscles equal use. For example, if you were to spend the entire day reading, you would have used your eye muscles to the point of exhaustion, but the muscles of your arms and legs would have been idle. This is why it is important for young people to play after school hours, and why businessmen who are in their offices all week should go in for some kind of physical activity in their free time. Muscles that are never used lose what is called muscle

Each one of the many muscles of the body has its own special shape. Each one is designed to suit the bone or tissue structure that it operates and to perform its specific tasks efficiently.

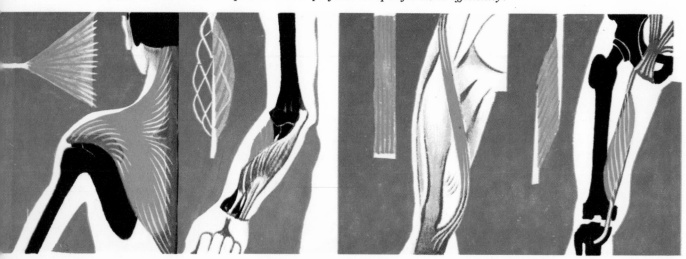

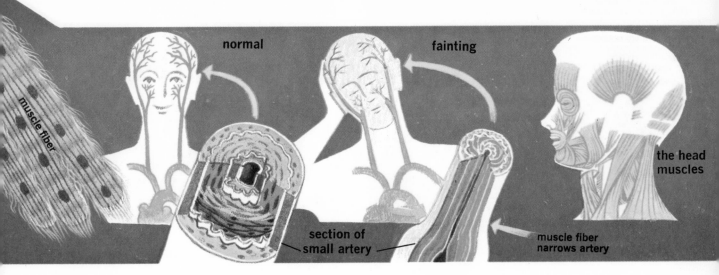

normal   fainting

muscle fiber

section of
small artery

the head
muscles

muscle fiber
narrows artery

Muscle fibers in the outer walls of arteries widen or narrow them. When the arteries leading to the brain are squeezed, less blood than usual flows through them. Dizziness and fainting result.

tone—they become flabby. When they are finally needed, they are so slack and weak that they can only come into play slowly and without power.

Muscles that have good tone can tighten quickly and strongly. This is one sign of a healthy body. A good way to think of tone is to think of a healthy plant. The stalks and leaves are firm when the plant cells are in good health, receive enough water, and are properly nourished. Otherwise the leaves droop and the stalks are limp—the plant generally looks unhealthy. When a person is tired, the muscles of the skin of his face are likewise slack and without the usual color and tone. We say that the person looks worn out.

In addition to muscle fatigue, many people, particularly athletes, often receive minor muscle injuries. Baseball pitchers are prone to sore arms which are really muscle strains. Football players often get bruised muscles from being tackled or sat upon. Generally a little rest, some time under a heat lamp, and massage by the trainer fixes them up. Aching muscles the day after strenuous exercise are common to everyone. Such activities as digging in the garden or rowing after a period of inactivity can make arms, legs, back, and abdominal muscles feel stiff and painful. The best remedy is more of the same exercise in small amounts until the discomfort wears off.

When a leg is broken and put into a cast to heal, its muscles become flabby and weak from lack of use. These muscles can be restored to their normal strength by proper exercise.

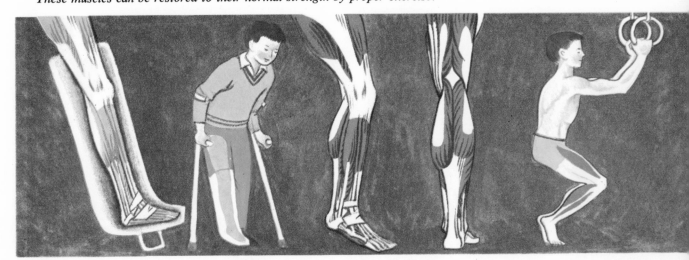

MUSCLES AND TENDONS OF HAND

Some of the tendons that help control the movements of the hand start far down in the forearm.

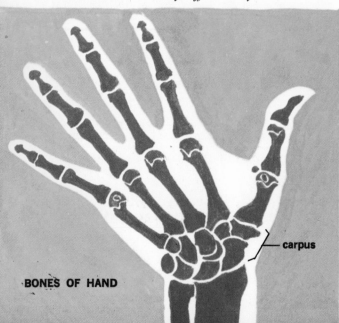

The most remarkable feature of the human hand is that it can be used in so many different ways.

— carpus

BONES OF HAND

Using Your Hands and Feet

Mᴀɴ belongs to the class of animals called mammals, but he is different enough to be thought of as a special creature. Among the things that make him very different are his ability to talk, and his hands. With his hands, man can do many things such as put up a house, play the piano, paint pictures, and perform surgical operations.

Of the 206 bones in the human body, approximately one-fourth—more than fifty—are in the hands. Bend your fingers a little so that you can count just the finger bones of one hand. There are fourteen of them. It is because there are so many that the fingers are so flexible.

The palm of the hand consists of a tough, fibrous sheet lying beneath the skin, attached to the muscles of the fingers and the ligaments of the wrist. It acts as a protective shield for the muscles, tendons, and nerves that run beneath it to the fingers. If it were not present, a ball could not be caught without hurting the hand. Grasping a bat tightly would probably be painful, too.

Move your wrist. Notice how easily it moves and makes possible all sorts of hand motions. The wrist is made up of eight small bones. None of them is bigger than a large wedding ring. These bones are kept in position by strong ligaments. A few of the muscles that move the fingers are attached to the bones, but their function is chiefly to make the wrist flexible.

A large number of muscles and tendons are needed to make the complicated bone structure of the hand work. Some of these start from the wrist bones and ligaments, and extend a few inches to the fingers. Many, however, start far down the forearm. You can feel them move when you clench your fist. These long muscles taper into thin, ribbonlike tendons that end in the fingers. The reason why hand and finger movements can be made with such accuracy and precision is that

The hands contain more than fifty bones, or about one-fourth of all the bones in the entire body.

there are twenty-eight muscles working each hand and its fingers. Compare this with the elbow, which needs only two muscles to move it back and forth!

The master of the hand is the thumb. It stands a little away from the rest of the fingers and partly faces them. The ability to hold or grasp depends on the power with which the thumb can press against the other fingers. It is easy to see how important the thumb is by trying to pick up a telephone book without using it. It can be done —but it's an awkward business.

The human hand is wonderfully made—and so is the human foot. The foot works as if it consisted

See for yourself how the foot acts. Stand with your feet slightly apart and slowly shift your weight back and forth from the heel to the ball. Then, standing with your weight forward, move your toes. You can even rock from the ball to the toes. You are moving your weight around on all points of the different springs.

In order to make all these motions possible, the bone structure of the foot is similar to that in the hand and wrist. The wrist, or carpus, has eight bones. The part of the foot like it, the tarsus, has seven. The foot's instep resembles the hand's arched palm and, like it, has five bones. The toes, like the fingers, have fourteen.

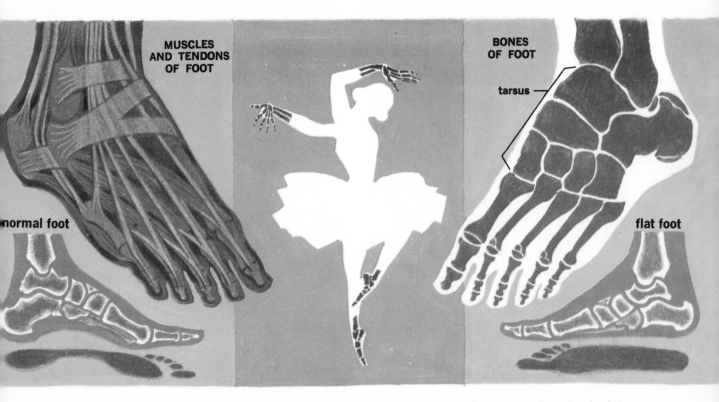

MUSCLES AND TENDONS OF FOOT

BONES OF FOOT

tarsus

normal foot

flat foot

The bones of the foot are arranged to support the weight of the body in many positions. Because the foot is so strong, a ballet dancer can balance herself and even whirl about on her toes.

of two springs, such as fine automobiles often have at their rear wheels. One spring extends from the toes to the heel, and the other stretches across the foot. Usually, the base of the toes is called the ball of the foot. Anyone who has ever looked at his footprint on wet sand, or seen the print left on the bathroom floor will have noticed that there are really two balls. One is just behind the big toe, and there is a smaller, flatter one behind the small toe. Each toe itself also acts as a spring.

The complicated arrangement of muscles, nerves, blood vessels, and ligaments already described for the hand occurs also in the foot. The main difference is that the foot, with its short toes and spring-like arches, is designed for walking, running, and jumping; the hand is designed to specialize in grasping.

All together, the bones of the hands, feet, and wrists total nearly half of all the bones in the entire human body.

How Your Body Knows What to Do

FEELING anything, knowing anything, and doing anything all depend on special tissues called nerves.

The skin of the human body is like the outer wall of a great fort. Different parts of the wall are connected to the main part of the fort by telephone wires. The telephones report what is going on in different places around the wall. People in the main part of the fort decide what to do. They call other parts of the fort and give orders. Telephones all over the fort keep each part aware of what is going on elsewhere.

The nerves in the body are like the fort's telephones.

Each kind of tissue is made up of its own particular kind of cells. Nerve tissue is made up of nerve cells. We are born with all the nerve cells we will ever have. If a nerve cell is somehow damaged, the nerve will not—like skin, bone, or muscle—produce a new cell to take its place.

Each nerve cell is composed of a cell body from which stem branches, or fibers. On one side are a number of short, twiglike branches called dendrites, from the Greek word for "tree." On the other side is a long branch knows as the axon. The nerves connect all the parts of the body with the brain or with the spinal cord.

The outer endings of the nerves are equipped with sensitive receptors. These receptors pick up impulses and send them to the main part of the nerve cell to be transmitted to the brain. In the skin, for example, receptors tell whether the skin is hot or cold, whether it is being pinched or tickled. The nerve cell then sends on this information by its axon to the brain. In the brain, the information is received and identified. If some sort of action is necessary, the brain determines what it is, and then sends out messages over the nerve to the muscles to carry it out.

When the brain gets a message through the nerve fibers that a certain part of the body is un-

Nerve fibers may be compared to telephone cables. Both transmit messages by electrical charges. The nerve cell is somewhat like a sparkplug, which lights up when an electrical current is passed through it.

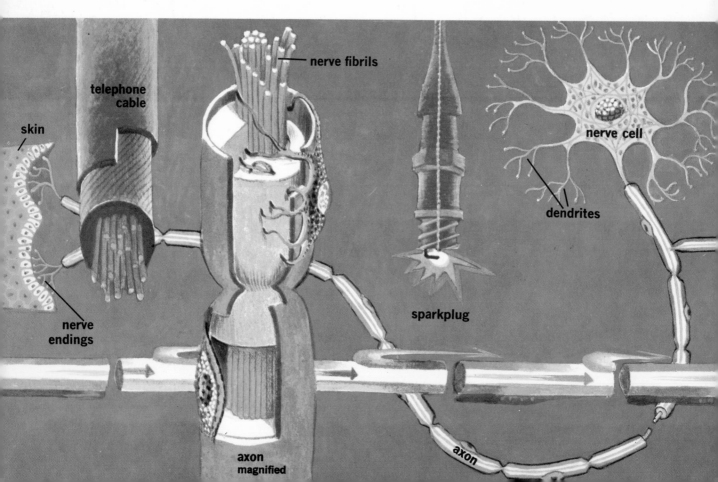

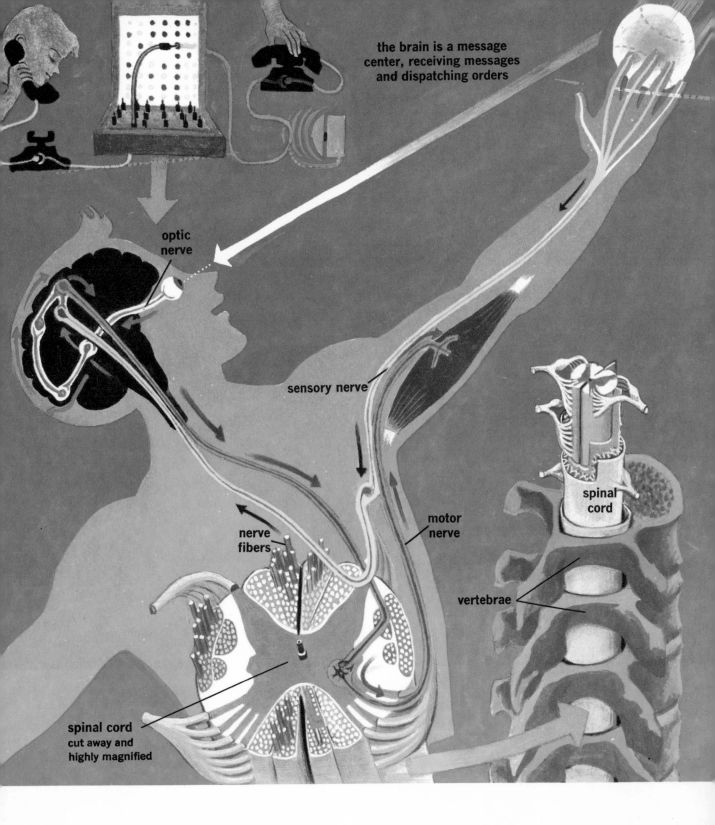

the brain is a message
center, receiving messages
and dispatching orders

optic
nerve

sensory nerve

spinal
cord

motor
nerve

nerve
fibers

vertebrae

spinal cord
cut away and
highly magnified

comfortable, then it may decide that the entire body should move to some other, more comfortable position. Once this decision is made, messages are sent through other nerves to the muscles that will move the body.

It is clear, then, that there must be two kinds of nerves. There are nerves that carry messages of

The nervous system is like a telephone switchboard. Messages pass through it to the brain, which orders the proper part of the body to react. In the illustration above, nerve endings in the skin report that they are touching the ball. The brain will relay a message for the fingers to close around and catch the ball. The eye has already sent a message along the optic nerve warning the brain that the ball is on its way.

Some reflex actions, like the one shown in the picture above, help protect the body from injury.

sensation to the brain. These tell the brain that the pin that sticks you hurts, or the stove you touch is hot. Because they carry messages of sensation, they are called sensory nerves. The messages from the brain are carried to muscles or glands by other nerves. These are called motor nerves because they carry messages ordering movement.

The body can move because of the way bones are joined. Muscles move the bones. Nerves carry the messages that tell the muscles when, where, and how to move the bones.

Anyone who has seen a telephone switchboard, or looked inside a television or radio set, has seen that the electrical wires are tied into bundles at certain places. Nerves, too, are grouped into bundles of fibers. Many of these nerves pass up to the brain through the hollow backbone. The bundle in the backbone makes up the spinal cord.

Sometimes messages are so simple that they don't have to go all the way to the brain for a

By tapping a patient's knee, doctors can tell whether or not his reflexes are working properly.

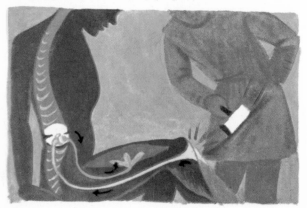

decision. For example, in the presence of something that is too hot, signals telling of immediate danger go to the spinal cord, and at once messages are sent from there to the proper muscles. Instantly the body pulls back. When the body reacts to nerve messages that do not have to go to the brain, the movement is called a reflex action.

The doctor makes use of reflex action in his examinations. Everyone has noticed how his leg jumps when the doctor taps it just below the kneecap. This is a good example of a reflex. The sensory nerve telegraphs a message to the spinal cord that the knee has been tapped. In the spine, a connector nerve picks up the message and transmits it to a motor nerve. The impulse travels over the axon of the motor nerve to the thigh muscle and signals it to contract. The muscle then flexes, producing the knee-jerk. This shows the doctor that the nerves and muscles of that part of the body are functioning normally.

In addition to the workings of the nerves already described and to reflexes, there is another, special nervous system to take care of motions that take place automatically. In breathing, for example, muscles work to pump the air into and out of the lungs. This is done without any conscious effort by the brain. Nerves keep these muscles pumping even during sleep.

There are also muscles in the stomach and intestines. The brain doesn't decide to make the stomach digest the food that goes into it, and it doesn't tell the intestine when and how to move food through itself.

The nerves that work automatically are different from the other nerves. The muscles they control are mostly the smooth, or involuntary, muscles that were described earlier.

There is still a great deal to be learned about the nerves; but it is well known that messages are sent from one nerve to another by electrical means. In fact, some of the earliest experiments with electricity were carried out on the leg of a frog. An Italian scientist over a hundred years ago showed that he could make the muscles of a frog's leg twitch and contract by giving a tiny electrical shock to the nerve. The man was Alessandro Volta. The word "volt," which is used in electricity, was coined in his honor.

How and Where You Think

THE PEOPLE of ancient times had very little notion of the importance of the brain. They thought, for instance, that courage stemmed from the heart and cowardice from the liver. Today we know that the brain controls all our actions. We know that the brain receives messages from all the body's organs and transmits messages to control glands and muscles.

The brain is a wonderful machine for learning. One of its greatest successes was to learn about itself. For a long time people thought that thinking was done in the heart. Now, however, we not only know that it takes place in the head, but doctors and scientists can even tell which part of the brain does a particular job.

Put one hand on your forehead and the other on the back of your head just above the neck. You are holding your brain in your hands. Then move your hands until your fingers are just behind your ears. Somewhere between the hands, the brain is connected with the spinal cord.

The surface of the brain is made of gray tissue.

Messages from all over the body come to the cells of the cerebellum, which lies below and behind the main part of the brain. Together with the inner ear, the cerebellum helps us stay on balance. It also coordinates muscles, keeping them ready to respond to nerve impulses.

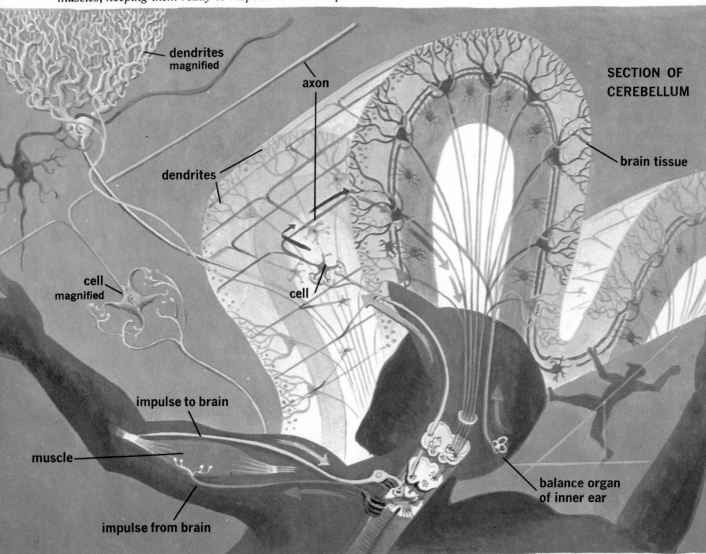

dendrites
magnified

axon

SECTION OF
CEREBELLUM

dendrites

brain tissue

cell
magnified

cell

impulse to brain

muscle

balance organ
of inner ear

impulse from brain

41

Underneath this layer the brain is white. Both the gray and the white parts are made of nerve tissue. Sometimes you will hear someone say of a very clever person, "He has plenty of gray matter."

The surface of the brain is slightly wrinkled in infants. As a person grows older, the wrinkles get deeper. In a full-grown man of average size, the brain weighs about three pounds. As people grow very old, the brain begins to get slightly smaller.

The part of the brain just behind the forehead is where we make plans, where we learn new things, where we remember, and where we decide between right and wrong. This part also brings together and coordinates memories stored in other parts of the brain. It is the part of the brain that is very much larger in man than in any other animal.

About halfway back, there is a deep groove—the central groove—that separates the front part of the brain from the rear. It runs roughly on a line between the ears. Just in front of this line is the brain's motor center, the part of the brain that gives orders to the muscles to move. Doctors and students of biology know which areas control the toes, feet, legs, thighs, and so on.

Behind this deep dividing line is the part of the brain that knows where and what we feel. This is the sensory center. Just as each part of the body has a special area in the motor center to control it, so each part has a special area in the sensory center that recognizes and identifies what it feels. The brain cells in these centers may be imagined in the form of a tiny, upside-down figure on the brain (as shown in the central picture, below). The cells that respond to stimulus in the lower parts of the body are toward the top of the brain, those for the upper parts of the body are lower down on the brain.

Below the sensory center, on a level with the ears, is a place in the brain that interprets sounds—the hearing center. In the back of the brain is the center for vision. The center for smell is in front of the center for hearing.

Certain parts of the brain develop more on one side than on the other. It is easy to see which side is dominant. In right-handed people, the left side of the brain is dominant. In left-handed people, it is the right side that is dominant. Some people can write or throw a ball equally well with left or right hand. They are called ambidextrous—from the Latin word meaning "double-right-handed." These people's brains are developed equally on both sides.

Underneath and behind the main part of the brain is another part, which is called the cere-

Thinking and feeling take place in various parts of the brain's outer tissue. The special areas for sensation and movement (as shown by small, human figure on brain, below) lie on opposite sides of the brain's central groove.

The brain's cells for sensation and movement are in reverse order—those that respond to stimulus in the feet are toward the top of the brain (A), while those that serve the head are lower down on the brain (B).

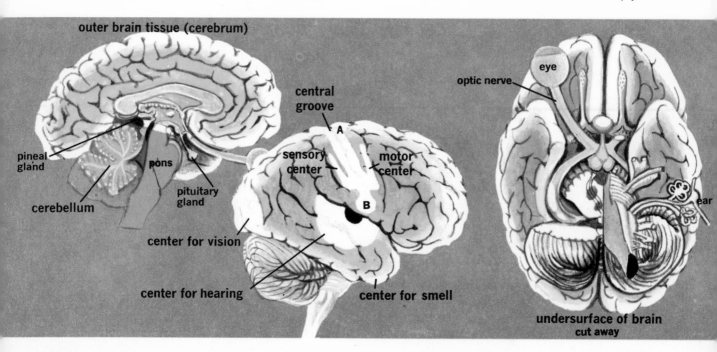

outer brain tissue (cerebrum)

central groove

A

sensory center

motor center

B

eye

optic nerve

pineal gland

pons

pituitary gland

cerebellum

center for vision

center for hearing

center for smell

ear

undersurface of brain
cut away

bellum, or "little brain." Its most important duty is to help the muscles work together. It also keeps the muscles ready to respond at once to signals to start moving. When muscles are sluggish, they don't obey nerve signals when they should. To keep our balance as we walk means that many muscles have to do their work faultlessly and in precisely the right order. Otherwise we would stumble and fall. The "little brain" keeps muscles ready to go, and coordinates them.

Sometimes people are annoyed that so many of the parts of the body have difficult-sounding names. Actually, there is good reason for this. Many of the names belong to languages that were used many thousands of years ago. The Romans, and the Greeks before them, knew most of the parts of the body, even though they didn't know how these parts worked. To them, the back of the head was simply "back of the head," and they called it *occiput*. Their name for "brain" was *cerebrum*, and for "little brain," *cerebellum*.

Like many other languages, the English language comes partly from Greek and Latin. It was natural for many Greek and Latin words to be used by people speaking English. Doctors especially adopted the custom of using Greek and Latin words for parts of the body. They did this

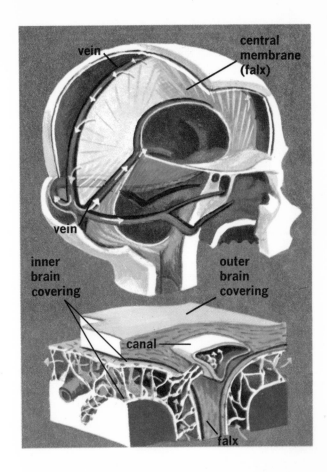

because it was natural to do so, and also because they knew that these words were well understood by other doctors in many different countries.

The brain ventricle (shown in green, below) is a fluid-filled section of the brain. There are four such ventricles in the brain. They contain fluid that flows around the brain and cushions it from shocks.

A curtainlike membrane—the falx—divides the brain in two. It runs from back to front and is shown here in three views, two in the picture above and one in the picture below. At its top and bottom are canals for veins.

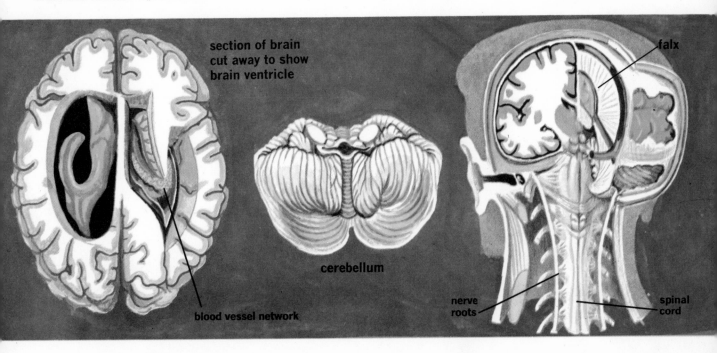

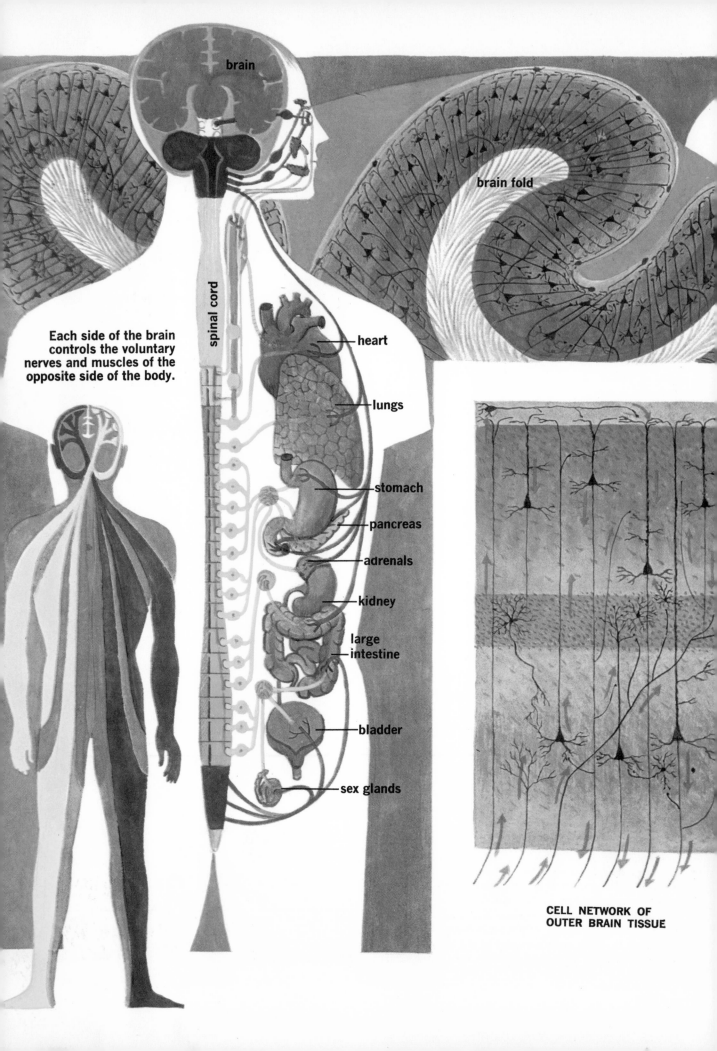

brain

brain fold

Each side of the brain controls the voluntary nerves and muscles of the opposite side of the body.

spinal cord

heart

lungs

stomach

pancreas

adrenals

kidney

large intestine

bladder

sex glands

CELL NETWORK OF OUTER BRAIN TISSUE

How You Know What You Know

ONE of the most terrible-tempered doctors of all time was Galen, who lived in the days of the Romans. He got into bitter fights with other doctors who disagreed with him, and put all his energy into making tests to prove that he was right. He was right a surprising number of times, but not so often as he thought.

From Galen's work, people first learned about the twelve most important nerves in the body. These are called the cranial nerves, and they are in pairs—one set for each side of the body.

These are the nerves that most directly report what is going on in the world about you. They all go directly to the brain. Galen discovered only a few, but he started the system—which we still use—of referring to them by number.

FIRST: The nerve that carries to the brain messages about smell. The brain's center for smell, or olfactory center, recognizes several types of odors, each type having several possible variations. For example, one of the types of odors is called "flowery," but the olfactory center can tell the difference between violet, rose, lilac, and honeysuckle. Another type of odor is called "burnt," but the brain can tell the difference between burning tobacco, roasted coffee, wood smoke, and burning paper. A third type is that of rotting substances. A fourth may be called "spicy"; it includes such fruity odors as apple, pear, lemon, orange, pineapple, and others. A fifth type of odor includes camphor, gasoline, alcohol, turpentine, and other chemicals. A sixth is called aromatic.

SECOND: The nerve that tells the brain about what is being seen.

THIRD: The nerve that controls five of the muscles that move the eye. When you are crossing a busy street and look from side to side, it is because the brain has signaled the third cranial nerve to move the eye so that it can report any danger through the second cranial nerve.

FOURTH: The nerve that controls the upper oblique muscle of the eye (see diagram, page 47).

FIFTH: A nerve with three different parts:

One part goes to the forehead and different places in the eye and the eyelid. It controls the

The first cranial nerve, known as the olfactory nerve, helps us identify different kinds of odors.

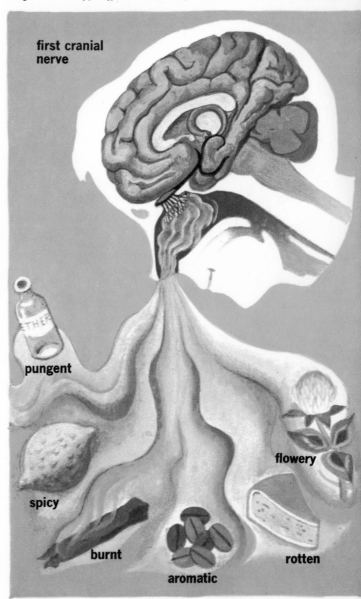

◄ *The brain is the headquarters for the body's nervous system. Nerves attached to its various parts transmit sensations received by sensory organs and carry impulses controlling many bodily functions. But it is the folded and wrinkled gray matter of the outer brain tissue that is perhaps the most important part of the human brain. Doctors think that all mental activities take place here.*

THE EYE IS LIKE A CAMERA

THE CRANIAL NERVES CONTROL THE EYE MUSCLES

THE EYE SEES UPSIDE DOWN

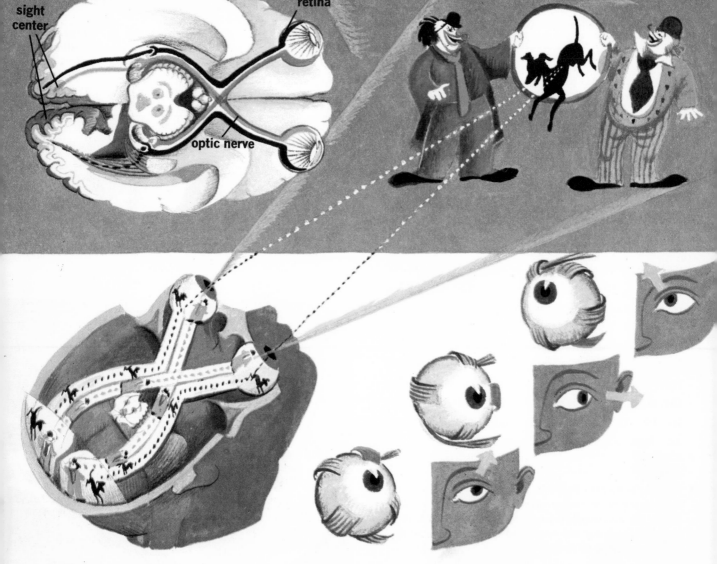

sight center

retina

optic nerve

The eye could not function—could not tell the brain what it sees, could not move, could not even close—without the cranial nerves that control it.

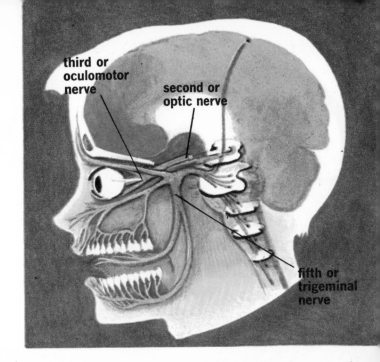

tears in crying and when the eye needs moistening. It also tells when the nose is running, and it is through this nerve that we feel the dry tickle when the nose is dried out.

The second part of this nerve has many branches, some of which go to the side of the nose, the lower eyelid, the upper lip, and the upper gums and teeth. It also goes to the palate and throat. If you run your tongue over your teeth to moisten them the wet feeling is carried to the brain by this part of the fifth nerve.

The third part of this nerve does the same thing as the second, but for the lower jaw, the tongue, the skin of the temple, the ear, and the lower part of the face. This nerve not only carries messages to the brain, but also transmits orders from the brain to signal the jaw muscle to chew.

At mealtime, the fifth nerve is particularly busy. It carries orders to chew, and also brings back the description of what it feels like to chew. In addition, if a cavity has formed in one of the teeth, it is this fifth nerve that aches with the news.

SIXTH: The nerve that controls the lateral muscle of the eye (see diagram, lower right).

SEVENTH: The nerve that controls the muscles of your face—to make you smile, for instance. It also brings taste sensations from the front part of the tongue to the brain.

EIGHTH: The nerve that carries to the brain the news we get by hearing. It has another part which tells the brain whether or not the body is balanced or falling, and in what direction it's going. It finds these things out from a tiny balance organ in the skull near the ear. When you stumble and then manage to regain your balance, it is because the eighth nerve has told your brain about the trouble, and your brain has signaled to your arms and legs to take care of the matter.

◄ *In many ways the eye works like a camera. Both eye and camera invert the image of the picture in front of them. When the eye sends this inverted image over the optic nerve to the brain, the brain corrects the image so that things appear to us as they really are.*

THE EYE'S CRANIAL NERVES

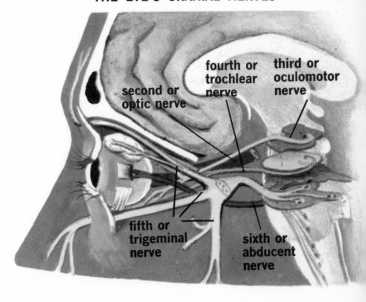

THE EYE MUSCLES

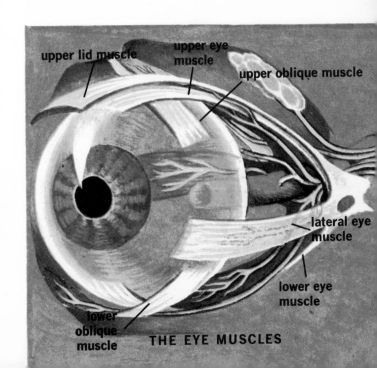

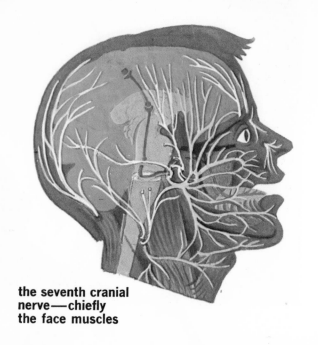

the seventh cranial nerve—chiefly the face muscles

NINTH: A nerve that has several jobs. One part of it goes to the tongue and, together with a branch of the seventh nerve, tells the brain what you taste. When you eat a piece of steak, for instance, it is this ninth nerve that tells the brain what steak tastes like. But steak gives pleasure, not only because of its taste but because of the way it feels in the mouth. The fifth tells the brain about that part of it as it seems to the teeth and jaws. The ninth has still another job: with the twelfth nerve, it controls the muscles of speech and allows you, when you hold out your plate, to ask for more.

TENTH: The only cranial nerve that passes into the chest and abdomen. It regulates heartbeat, breathing, and digestion without our having to stop to think about it to keep the body alive.

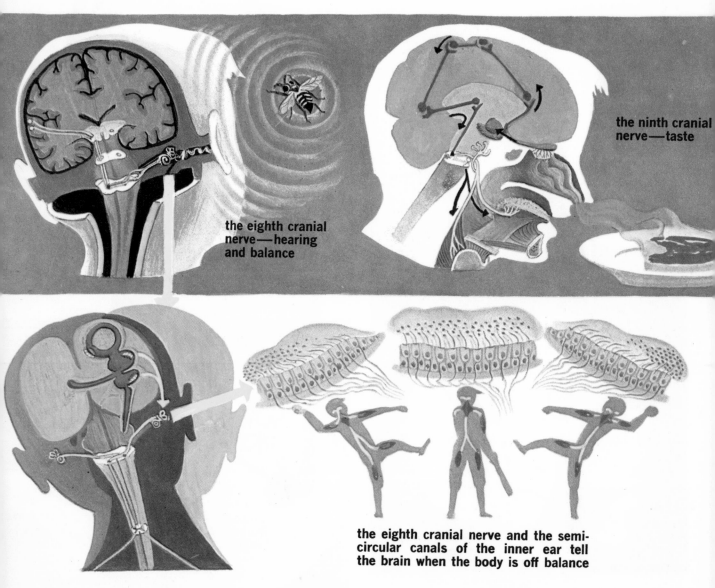

the eighth cranial nerve—hearing and balance

the ninth cranial nerve—taste

the eighth cranial nerve and the semi-circular canals of the inner ear tell the brain when the body is off balance

ELEVENTH: The nerve that carries signals to the muscles of the neck and back that turn the head and shoulders.

TWELFTH: The nerve that carries messages of movement to the tongue. You use it to talk, and to put out your tongue for the doctor.

For primitive man, the information that came through these nerves meant the difference between life and death. His eyes showed him the presence of enemies as well as of food in the form of growing things, game animals, and fish. His ears helped him identify the same things. Odors and taste indicated whether food and drink were safe to consume. Climbing trees and running were made safer by messages giving information about balance. And even today, many of these functions are still important to us.

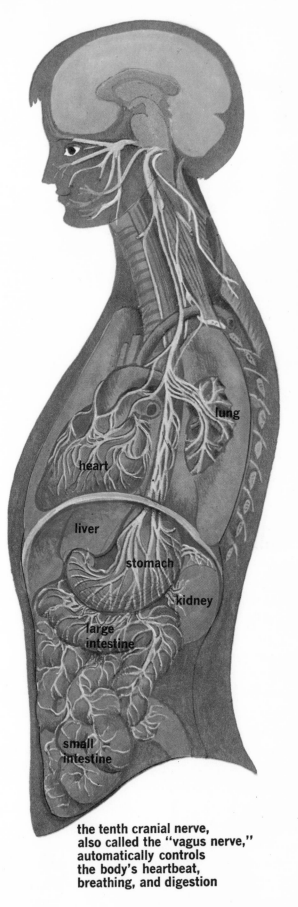

lung

heart

liver

stomach

kidney

large intestine

small intestine

the tenth cranial nerve, also called the "vagus nerve," automatically controls the body's heartbeat, breathing, and digestion

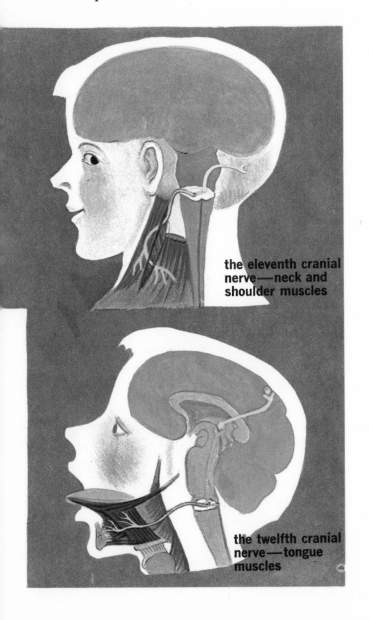

the eleventh cranial nerve—neck and shoulder muscles

the twelfth cranial nerve—tongue muscles

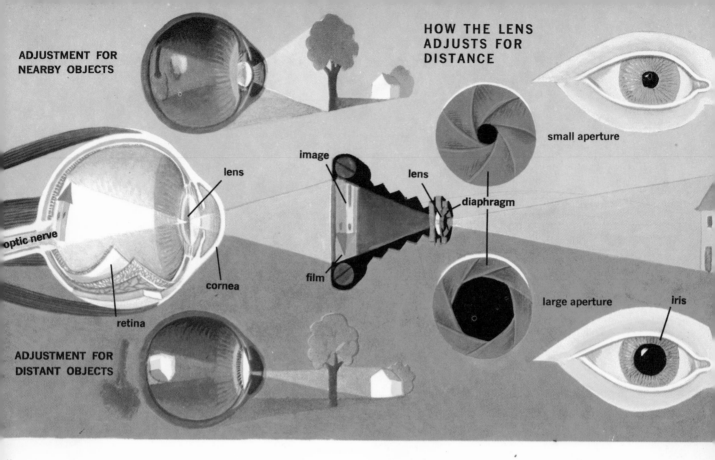

ADJUSTMENT FOR
NEARBY OBJECTS

HOW THE LENS
ADJUSTS FOR
DISTANCE

small aperture

image

lens

lens

diaphragm

optic nerve

film

cornea

large aperture

iris

retina

ADJUSTMENT FOR
DISTANT OBJECTS

Seeing the World

Even though men have known for hundreds of thousands of years what the eye does, they haven't always known how it works. Even in the time of the Romans, doctors didn't know. We still use Latin names for many parts of the eye, but through the years these words have taken on entirely new meanings.

Everybody knows that cameras have lenses. Today the word "lens" means a specially shaped piece of clear glass that gathers light into a bright, sharp spot. The lens of the eye does just that, and although we use the Roman word for it, the Romans didn't know what the lens did. They just knew it was part of the eye. Their word for it was based on its shape—like a small round bean—and the meaning of *lens* to the Romans was "bean." Hundreds of years before the Romans, the Greeks, too, knew about the lens, but because the lens was clear their name for it was "little piece of ice."

Now that cameras are so widely used, most people also understand how the eye works. A camera is a box that allows light to come in only at one place. In this place is a lens. Through the lens comes light from the scene that is directly in front of the camera. The light travels straight to the back of the camera, where it hits the film. On the film is a thin layer of chemical which darkens when light falls on it. The greater the amount of light, the greater the amount of darkening. Since different amounts of light come from different parts of the scene in front of the camera, the film is darkened unevenly. The mixture of dark and light spots on the film is what makes the picture.

In the eye, the lens, just behind the cornea, allows light to shine on a layer of tissue at the back of the eyeball. This tissue is covered by a network of blood vessels. The Latin name for it—*retina*—meant "net" and is still used today. The retina, like the film in a camera, is changed by light shining on it.

The film in a camera must be changed for each picture, but the eye keeps on using the same

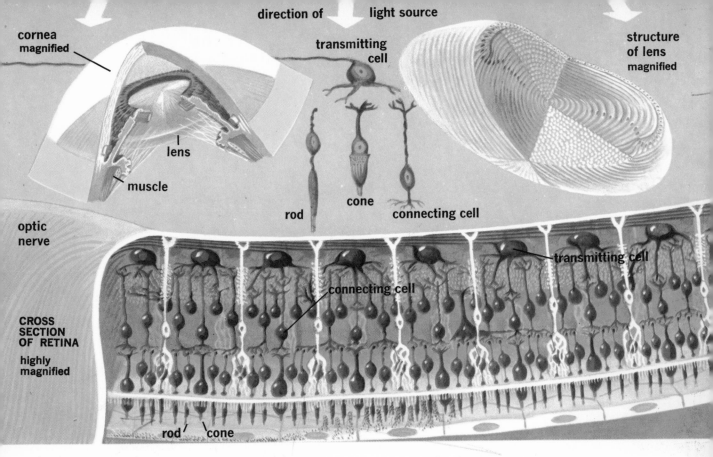

direction of light source

cornea
magnified

transmitting
cell

structure
of lens
magnified

lens

muscle

cone

rod

connecting cell

optic
nerve

transmitting cell

connecting cell

CROSS
SECTION
OF RETINA
highly
magnified

rod   cone

*Light coming in through the lens of the eye shines on the retina in the back of the eye. Tiny rods and cones
in the retina pick out objects in black and white as well as in colors. A tough, clear covering called the
cornea lies over the iris and pupil and protects the lens.*

tissue. This tissue is really a layer of very fine
nerve cells of two kinds. Some of these cells are
shaped like tiny rods and recognize dimly outlined
objects. Others, shaped like cones, distinguish
colors and give sharp focus to vision. Sometimes
a person is said to be color-blind. This means
that some of the color-sensitive material is missing
from his eye, or is not functioning properly.

Once the light reaches the rods and cones, the
eye sends the message of what it sees to the optic
nerve. This nerve is the second cranial nerve, and
it is along this cable that sight messages are sent
to the brain. When the brain decides what to do
about the news it is getting, messages are sent to
the muscles of the body. They carry out whatever
decision the brain has deemed necessary or advisable. In a game of jacks, the brain, acting on the
eye's message, tells the hand to pick up the right
number of pieces before the ball bounces. In
baseball, the message from the eye causes the
brain to tell the hands to catch the ball.

The lens is protected by a covering, the cornea.
Between the lens and the retina is a clear, thick
liquid filling the ball of the eye. This liquid helps
the lens bend the light to form a large picture of
the scene in front of the eye. To be able to see as
much without this liquid in the eyeball, the eye
would have to be several times larger than it is.

One of the most remarkable features of the eye
is that it can move so easily. Six muscles move
each eye—up and down, from side to side. Another set of muscles, attached to each lens, make
the lens thick for viewing nearby objects, or thin
for viewing distant ones. Still other muscles widen
or narrow the opening of the eye to let in the
proper amount of light.

The eye is set well within the head and is protected by the bones of the skull. A small part of
the front can be seen through two hoods of flesh
called the eyelids.

The eyes of any two people are about the same
size. When someone is said to have large eyes, it

51

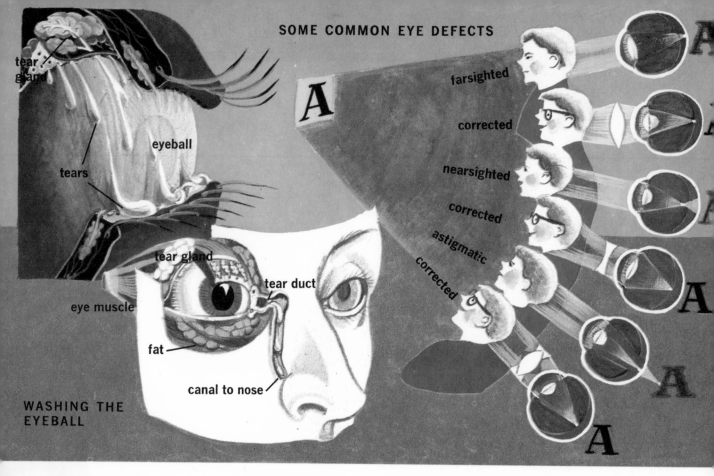

tear gland

eyeball

tears

tear gland

tear duct

eye muscle

fat

canal to nose

WASHING THE
EYEBALL

farsighted

corrected

nearsighted

corrected

astigmatic

corrected

Tear glands in a corner of the eye near the nose produce salty drops that bathe the eyeball. These drops then drain through tiny openings into the nose.

When the lens of the eye does not focus the image directly on the retina, the vision is blurred. Many such eye defects can be corrected with the proper kind of eyeglasses.

is only that the opening between the lids is larger than usual. In the lid, touching the upper corner of the eye, away from the nose, there is a small gland that produces the fluid we call tears. This fluid is slightly salty and continually bathes the eyeball, keeping it moist. The fluid drains off through a pair of tiny openings at the corner of the eye near the nose, and flows down through the nose.

Sometimes the salty fluid is produced so fast that not all of it can drain off this way. Then the overflow of drops tumbles directly from the eye. This happens when a piece of dust is stuck to the cornea and the pain causes tears to flow. It also happens when a person cries.

Just as a camera sometimes takes a fuzzy picture, so the eye sometimes makes a blurred image. A camera takes a bad picture if the lens is not the right distance from the film. In the eye, the lens is always the same distance from the retina, but the lens muscles can change the shape of the lens. Vision is blurred when the muscles cannot make

the lens the right shape. A person with normal eye lenses and muscles can plainly see things that are both near and far. When only those things that are far away can be plainly seen, the person is called farsighted. Someone is said to be nearsighted when he can see only those things that are very close.

Only within the past few hundred years has it been possible to help people with poor vision. The invention of eyeglasses is one of the greatest boons to man. Now there are glasses to correct many kinds of visual trouble. People who once would have been considered half blind can now see quite well with the aid of glasses.

If your eyes do not work properly, the tests given by your eye doctor will show what kind of help you need. The eyeglasses that are prescribed for you will have this help built in.

In addition to eyeglasses, there are other ways of helping people with poor vision. There are, for example, contact lenses which are fitted to the eyeball and serve the same purpose as eyeglasses.

52

Hearing and Balance

CLOSE YOUR eyes and listen to the world. Perhaps a clock is ticking in the next room. In another room a girl may be laughing, or a radio playing music. Outside, small harbor waves may be breaking against the beach. The world is full of sound wherever you go, and you can get a good idea of what is going on just by listening and using your imagination.

What is sound, and how is it heard?

Take a piece of tissue paper, hold it against a comb with your lips, and hum a tune. The tissue paper will change your voice, making it higher if the paper is held tightly, lower if the paper is held loosely. It will also add a new rasping sound. Your lips will feel a tickling from the paper, which flutters very lightly as you hum. That fluttering is called vibration. It is the vibration of the tissue paper that has made your voice sound different.

Sound itself is vibration of the air; and it is made by something vibrating in the air—like the tissue paper. The ear is able to hear because it

The world around us is filled with both strange and familiar sounds. Even with our eyes closed, we can tell what is going on simply by listening.

changes air vibrations into nerve messages which it sends to the brain.

A small child, learning the parts of his body, points to his nose, lips, and ears. He grows up believing that the part of the ear that was touched is all the ear there is. Actually the shell of flesh that was touched is the least important part of the human ear. Most of the ear is inside the head, where it is protected by the bones of the skull.

The outer ear is really a funnel which collects the sound vibrations from the outside world—the singing, laughing, talking, and all the other sounds we know. The ear funnel ends in a cave hollowed

Blowing through a comb covered with tissue paper makes the air going through the paper vibrate. The vibrations cause sound waves to be set up.

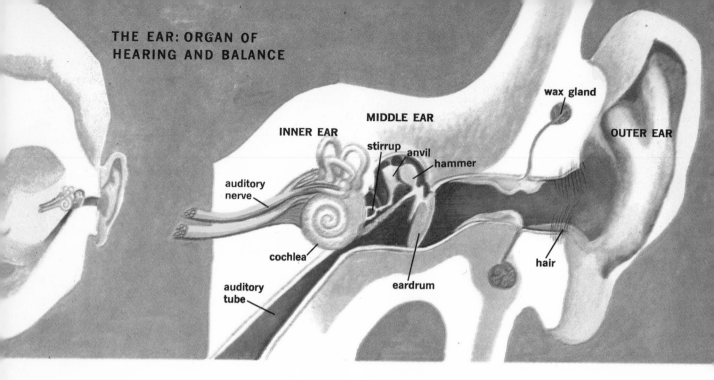

INNER EAR

MIDDLE EAR

OUTER EAR

wax gland

stirrup

anvil

hammer

auditory nerve

cochlea

auditory tube

eardrum

hair

out of the skull inside the head. This cave, called the middle ear, is closed by a thin, tight sheet of tissue called the eardrum. The eardrum acts somewhat like the sheet of tissue placed against the comb. The vibrating sound makes it flutter.

On the inner side of the eardrum is a set of three bones in a row. Because of their shapes, these small bones are called "hammer," "anvil," and "stirrup." The fluttering of the eardrum makes the hammer beat on the anvil, and the anvil vibrates against the stirrup, which is anchored by fibrous tissue to the opening of the inner ear still deeper in the skull.

In the inner ear there are two unrelated parts: the cochlea, which houses the true organ of hearing, and the semicircular canals, which help us to maintain balance. Cochlea means "snail's shell" in Latin, and that is what it looks like.

The inner ear is entirely filled with fluid. The vibrating waves of sound in the air cause the stirrup bone to vibrate against the membrane that separates the middle and inner ear. This causes waves to be set up in the fluid of the inner ear. The waves pass over the cells and the sensitive, hairlike nerve endings in the cochlea, where they are converted into nerve impulses that are taken to the brain by the eighth cranial nerve.

Poor hearing or complete deafness can result from trouble in any part of the hearing apparatus.

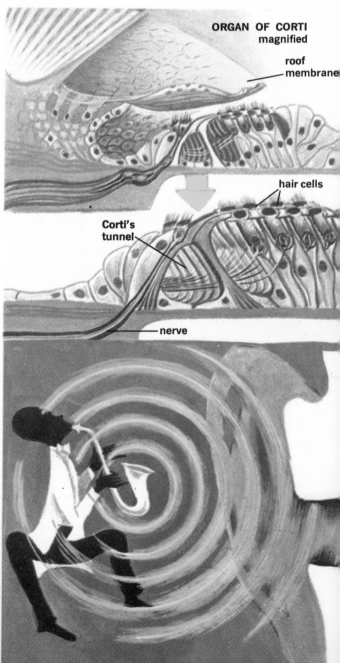

ORGAN OF CORTI
magnified

roof membrane

hair cells

Corti's tunnel

nerve

If wax forms in the ear, this can interfere with hearing. If the eardrum becomes torn or inflamed, hearing may diminish temporarily. If the eardrum is thickened or has a hole in it, hearing may always be poor on that side of the head. This can also happen if the bones of the middle ear are damaged by an infection. Going still deeper into the ear, there are cases where the membrane that separates the middle and inner ear is hardened. In addition to this, there can be a disorder of the cells in the cochlea itself, which may cause partial or total deafness. Finally, deafness can be caused by damage to the eighth cranial nerve, or by damage to the brain itself.

Hearing aids help many cases of deafness. We are all familiar with the picture of the old lady straining to catch every word with her ear trumpet. Nowadays, however, we have more effective modern devices that collect the sound and magnify it electrically, and then deliver it to the ear. In recent years it has even been possible to make these hearing aids so small that they can be built right into a pair of eyeglasses where they are practically invisible. The batteries weigh little more than a box of wooden safety matches. Hearing aids are of two types: those that fit into the ear and blow sound at the little ear bones for them to transmit to the inner ear, and those that lie directly on the bone behind the ear and send sound impulses through bone to the inner ear.

At times, of course, hearing aids are not enough help for people with poor hearing. In some cases operations on the ear may be necessary. If a person is born completely deaf and mute, even an operation may not help. Such a person may have to learn to communicate with others by sign language. People who are only partially deaf usually become skilled at reading other people's lips.

A chain reaction that takes place in the parts of the ear allows us to hear. Sound entering the outer ear strikes the eardrum and sets it vibrating. From here, the hammer and anvil transmit the vibrations to the stirrup, which is connected to the fluid-filled inner ear. In the inner ear is the cochlea, the true organ of hearing. It contains the organ of Corti and the delicate, flexible roof membrane. The fluid of the inner ear carries the sound impulses to the roof membrane and the sensitive hair cells of the organ of Corti. The impulses are changed to nerve signals and are then transmitted by nerves to the brain.

CROSS SECTION THROUGH COCHLEA
highly magnified

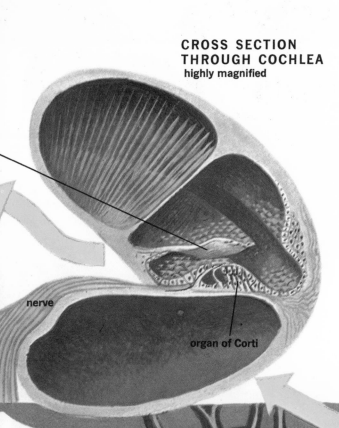

nerve

organ of Corti

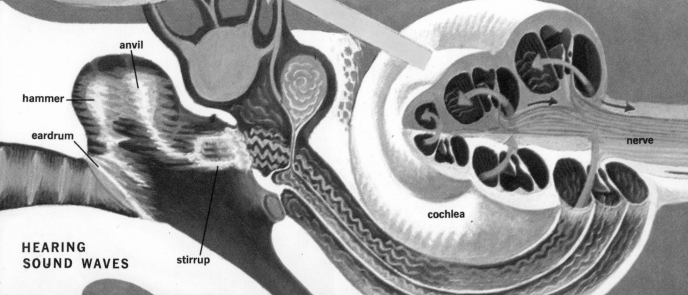

anvil

hammer

eardrum

nerve

cochlea

HEARING SOUND WAVES

stirrup

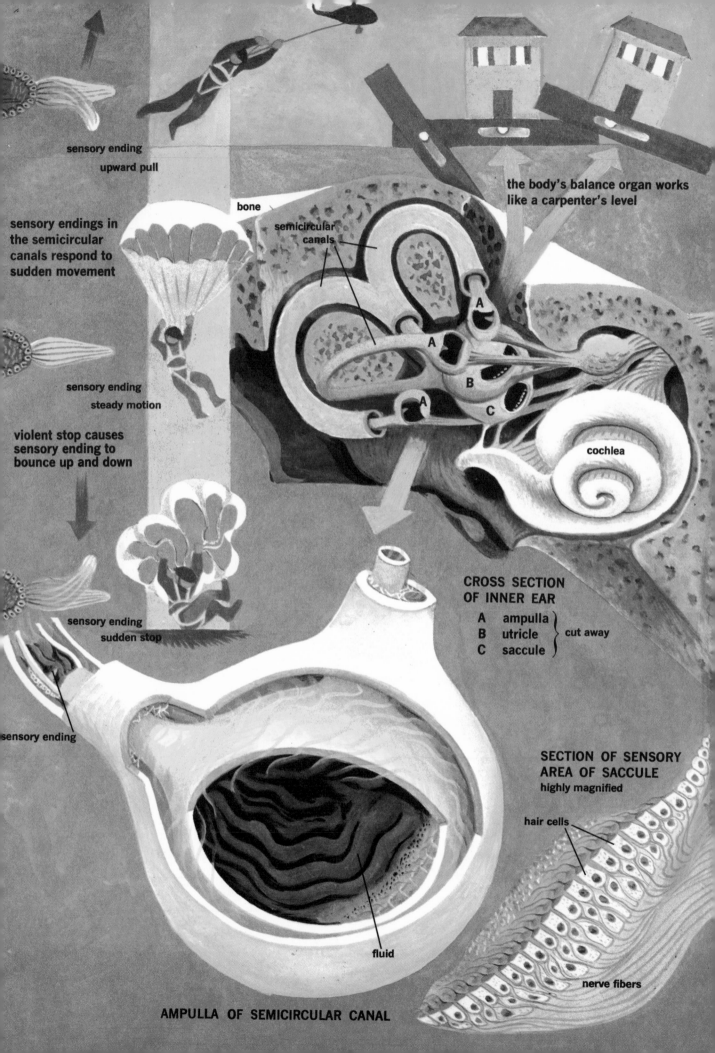

sensory ending
upward pull

sensory endings in
the semicircular
canals respond to
sudden movement

bone

semicircular
canals

the body's balance organ works
like a carpenter's level

A

A

A

B

C

A

cochlea

sensory ending
steady motion

violent stop causes
sensory ending to
bounce up and down

sensory ending
sudden stop

sensory ending

**CROSS SECTION
OF INNER EAR**

A ampulla
B utricle   } cut away
C saccule

**SECTION OF SENSORY
AREA OF SACCULE**
highly magnified

hair cells

fluid

nerve fibers

AMPULLA OF SEMICIRCULAR CANAL

The other important part of the inner ear has nothing at all to do with hearing. It consists of the semicircular canals which tell you whether or not you are off balance and, if you are off balance, which way.

An odd thing about the history of science is that long before men knew much about the human body, they had to work out most of the tricks that the body uses to stay alive. Men knew what lenses do with light long before they knew they had a lens in their own eyes. They knew about levers before they understood how bones moved. They could make things level long before they knew how the human body keeps itself balanced.

Men could not build sturdy houses, walls, forts, or ships without some way of being sure that the bricks and planks were level. The house you live in was built by carpenters who used an instrument called a level. Levels very like those used today have been used for centuries. In a level, the main part is a slightly curved glass tube filled with liquid, except for one bubble. When the level is held so that the tube ends slant downward, the bubble moves to the highest part of the tube. If the two ends of the tube are at exactly the same level, the bubble is in the exact center of the tube.

The semicircular canals of the inner ear are three curved tubes of bone. They are placed as shown in the pictures.

These three tubes are filled with liquid. Tiny organs in the walls of the tubes tell which way the liquid is moving. These organs send impulses to the brain over a branch of the eighth cranial nerve, but one that has nothing to do with the branch that transmits impulses for the sense of hearing. If you spin very quickly for a few seconds, then stop, the liquid continues moving in the tubes and impulses continue going to the brain. The room may seem to spin for a few seconds, and your stomach may suddenly feel as if it were upset. This is dizziness.

◄ *The three semicircular canals of the inner ear help keep the body balanced. Each canal is a loop partly filled with fluid. Each one has an enlarged end called an ampulla, which contains nerve endings and tiny hair cells. When the body is off balance, the hairs in the ampulla are set in motion by waves in the fluid around them. They signal the nerves that tell the brain to balance the body.*

The Sense of Smell

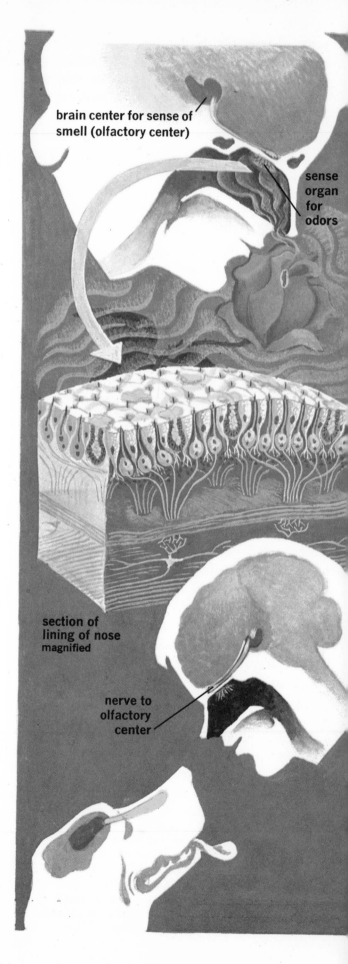

brain center for sense of smell (olfactory center)

sense organ for odors

section of lining of nose magnified

nerve to olfactory center

THE FLESHY part of the nose is, of course, only an outside covering. The section of the nose that actually detects odors is well inside the face, below the level of the eyes. In this region are the fine nerves, the tiny hairlike branches of the first cranial nerve which leads to the brain.

You cannot smell anything if the lining of your nose is dry. Cells are so made that they really belong to a fluid world, and this is true of the nerve cells that pick up odors. Usually the inside of the nose is lined with a thin layer of fluid called mucus. Any substance that gives off odors releases them in the form of tiny particles of vapor or gas. When these particles, or molecules, reach the nose, they are moistened by the mucus. Then they can be smelled.

When the nose is clogged with too much mucus, as when you have a cold, you have trouble smelling. This is because the tiny particles do not travel into the nose far enough to reach the nerve cells.

Much of what you think you taste in your mouth is really being smelled. After each swallow, the back of the nose is opened to the back of the throat; and odors of the food reach the nose at about the same moment that food is being tasted. Since smell and taste come together, one is often mistaken for the other.

Some of the greatest delights of living are the wonderful odors found in the world. The sense of smell, however, like all the other senses, is meant to do far more than give pleasure. The nerves of smell carry to the brain the message of pleasant food. The brain then sends the signal to the stomach. It tells the stomach that food is on the way and that the stomach must be ready to give out special juices to digest the food. The sense of smell in all animals is really a call to the stomach saying "Get ready!" Of course, if the food's odor

Odors come into the nose as vapors or gas. They are dissolved in a layer of fluid and stimulate special cells that carry the sensation of smell to the brain. The olfactory center, or center for smell, in a dog's brain is more sensitive than that found in a human.

58

seems disagreeable, the stomach may not get ready and the food will probably not be so well digested.

The sense of smell has other uses that are necessary for living. Animals use it not only to find food, but to tell them when creatures dangerous to them are near. Many animals depend on the sense of smell far more than we do. They need it to stay alive and keep well fed.

The sense of smell has one peculiarity. The nerve cell becomes accustomed to one particular odor so quickly that after the first few minutes it stops sending the message about that odor to the brain. The cell can reach the point where it no longer notices an odor that only a short time before it found very bad. But the same nerve cell can immediately send a message to the brain when a new odor appears.

This is why we find ourselves "getting used to" certain odors. It doesn't make any difference whether the odor is sweet or bad—we soon get used to it unless the substance causing the odor is actually hurting the nose. Getting used to odors is good for people who have to keep on working in a place full of bad odors. It is not good in cases where the odor is a danger signal.

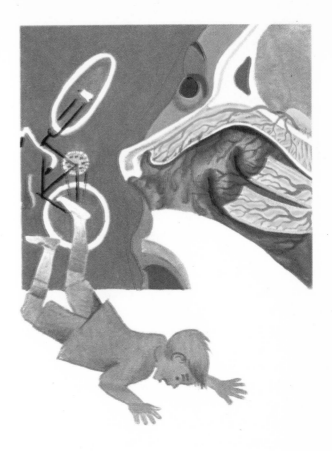

The nose has other important functions besides detecting odors. The dampness in its inner surface moistens and warms the air going to the lungs, making it less irritating to the delicate membranes of the windpipe. Small hairs in the nose, covered with sticky mucus, act as strainers to remove dust particles from the air as it passes through. Of course, not all the dust is trapped in the nose. Some reaches the lungs which have their own devices to remove impurities.

The nose may also be sensitive to types of particles in the air other than odors. For example, when some people inhale grains of pollen from certain plants, or little flakes of skin from dogs or cats, they get what is called an allergic reaction. The substance inhaled causes the membrane lining the nose to swell and secrete a watery fluid. This makes breathing just as difficult as a cold does.

The nose is a delicate instrument. A sharp blow may break some of the blood vessels that line it, causing a nosebleed. When the lining is inflamed or irritated, it becomes swollen and secretes a watery liquid. This is what happens during a cold.

The Taste Buds

THE SENSE of taste is located in the tongue, which does the tasting by means of special cells on its surface. These cells, called taste buds, are close to the surface of the upper part of the tongue. Human beings have about 3000 taste buds. Small fibers almost like tiny hairs extend from these cells to the surface of the tongue. They are so small that they can't be seen without the help of a powerful microscope.

The taste buds lie in little projections on the surface of the tongue called papillae. There are three kinds of papillae. Some are shaped like tiny mushrooms, others look like miniature hills with moats around them, and finally there are tiny threadlike or conical ones. In general, only the first two kinds of papillae contain taste buds.

The taste buds themselves all look alike, but doctors think there are four different types, one for each of the four primary tastes—sweet, sour, bitter, and salt. The buds for these four primary tastes are not spread evenly over the tongue. Instead, they are apparently grouped in special places. The front, or tip of the tongue, picks out all flavors, but particularly salt and sweet. Sour substances are best tasted along the sides of the tongue, and bitter things toward the back. The tongue tastes salt one-third of a second after it has come into contact with the taste bud. It takes a full second to taste something bitter.

Most foods contain mixtures of the four primary tastes, so blended that they have special flavors of their own. The flavor of lemonade, for example, is a combination of the sour of the lemon with the sweet of the sugar—and probably with traces

On the surface of the tongue are about 3000 tiny cells called taste buds. Different taste buds tell us when we are tasting something salty, sour, sweet, or bitter. These cells are located along the rim and across the back of the tongue. In the middle is a large area where nothing is tasted.

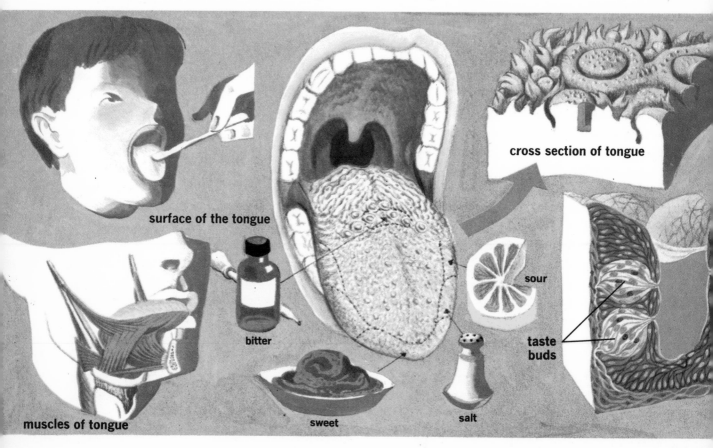

surface of the tongue

cross section of tongue

bitter

sour

taste buds

muscles of tongue

sweet

salt

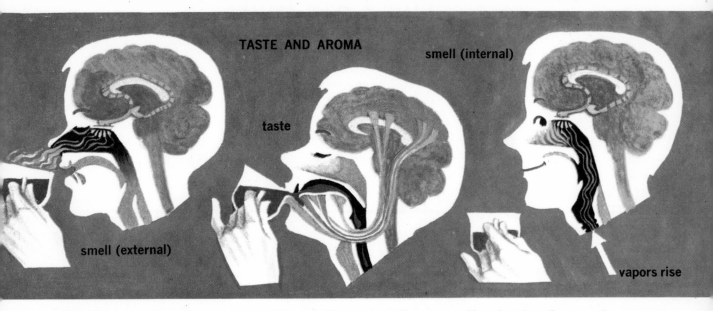

TASTE AND AROMA

smell (internal)

taste

smell (external)

vapors rise

Much of what we think we taste, we actually smell. Vapors rising from a cup of hot chocolate, for example, give an idea of how the drink will taste. As the chocolate is being drunk, vapors rise along the back of the throat. Much more than the taste buds, the nose gives an idea of how the drink "tastes."

of the other two primary tastes as well. However, most of the flavor of food is not recognized by the sense of taste at all. It is recognized instead by the sense of smell. By holding the nose when tasting something unpleasant, the taste is made to seem nowhere near so bad as it would otherwise be. Also, when the nose is clogged up, as with a cold, all food tastes flat even though the taste buds may be working perfectly normally.

Some people are better at tasting things than are others. This may be due to more sensitive taste buds, or it may be due simply to practice. Professional tasters, whether they specialize in cheese, tea, or wine, learn to taste large numbers of samples and remember most of them and how they differ from other, similar samples. This ability, however, is largely a matter of training the mind to remember tastes the way other people remember the words and melodies of songs.

The ability to taste certain things, scientists now think, is possibly inherited. Experiments with a chemical known as PTC (phenylthiocarbamide) showed that people fall into three groups. In one group, taking in most of the people who tasted the chemical, PTC was found to have a horribly bitter taste. Those in the third group considered it to have no taste whatsoever, while the second group fell in between. Different foods also tasted different to members of the three groups.

The receptors for the sense of taste, like those for the sense of smell, cannot work at all unless the substance they are working on is in a fluid state. When something perfectly dry is placed on the tongue, there is absolutely no taste. However, the tongue is covered by a special liquid that flows into the mouth from glands in the cheeks and under the tongue. This liquid, which is mostly water, is saliva. Food particles are moistened by saliva, and then they can be tasted. These saliva-making glands sometimes become infected and swell up. One such infection is called the mumps.

Tasting delicious food is one of the pleasures of living, but the mouth has a more important job to do than give pleasure. It is fulfilling nature's way of enticing you into doing the necessary work of eating.

Even if the tongue couldn't taste, we would still need it for other purposes. It helps to move food about in our mouths while we are chewing. Then, when we are ready to swallow the food, the tongue presses against the hard palate at the top of the mouth and pushes the food into the throat. There, powerful muscles take over and move the food down the food tube, or esophagus, into the stomach. The tongue can do all this chiefly because it is made up of strong muscle. The tongue also helps us to form the different sounds we use in speaking.

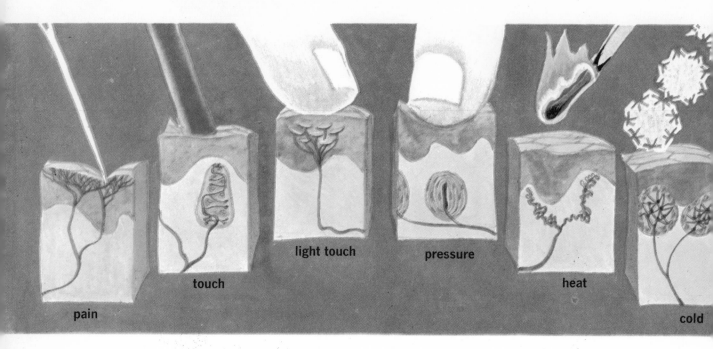

pain touch light touch pressure heat cold

Touch Signals

ALL THAT stands between you and the outside world, you might say, is your skin. The skin provides a number of ways of knowing what the outside world is like, and whether at any moment it is a safe or a dangerous place. The sense of pain in your skin makes you jump away when you touch something sharp. The sense of warmth makes you back away from too much heat. When it is cold, your skin warns you to put on more clothing. This is simply another way of saying that the skin, by its ability to feel different sensations, protects the body from harm.

The skin reports these sensations through special organs imbedded in it. Each organ is specialized to detect cold, warmth, pain, or simple pressure. These tiny warning devices work some-

The sense of touch works much like an electrical circuit. Contact between a finger and an object "closes" the circuit to the brain, and the nerve cells, like a light bulb, register the sensation.

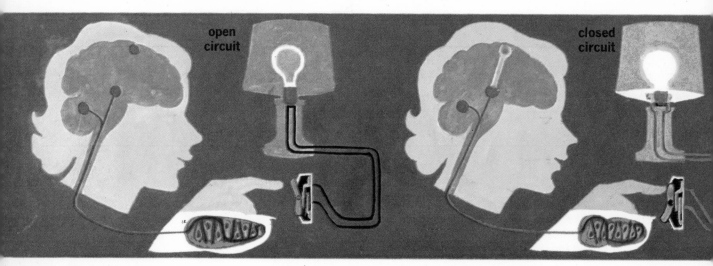

open circuit closed circuit

what like electric push buttons that send signals through the nerves to the spinal cord, and eventually to the brain. If the signal is painful, as from a pin prick or a hot stove, a reflex action may be set up. If a hand gets close to a hot stove, for example, this is reported to the nervous system. A motor nerve then stimulates the muscles to contract and withdraw the hand from the stove. In such a case the hand is withdrawn unconsciously. This is an example of a reflex action that begins in the skin.

In the skin there are twelve groups of cells to feel coldness as well as seventy-eight to feel heat. In addition, separate clusters of special sensory organs feel moving air currents, respond to stroking or tickling, or tell of movements by the skin.

So many different sensations come to us through the skin that it would be more correct to speak of perhaps a dozen senses of touch instead of only a single one.

Not all sensations, however, come from the skin. The muscles, bones, and internal organs are all supplied with nerves that give us information we need to know. Muscles, tendons, and joints contain detectors that report the positions of the muscles during activity. This allows the coordination and control of arms in swinging a baseball bat or a tennis racket. We are not aware of these sensations when we swing the bat. Some of them are so subtle that they produce their effect without our ever being able to say "I felt something." Muscles also have pain detectors that record pinching and squeezing, but not cutting or pricking. This is why injections, when they are made into the muscles, are hardly felt.

Vibration is another type of sensation. It may be experienced by holding the base of an ordinary tuning fork, which has been started vibrating, against the kneecap. A feeling like a buzzing will occur in the knee as long as the fork continues to vibrate. The organs that detect this type of sensation probably lie in the bone and its coverings, and in the tendons, though they may also be in the skin.

In the skin alone there are more than forty-five miles of nerves. They report heat, cold, and pressure to the centers of the brain. The body has other nerves that report sights, smells, and sounds to the brain.

Braille allows the blind to read. Tiny nerve endings in the fingers do the work for the eyes.

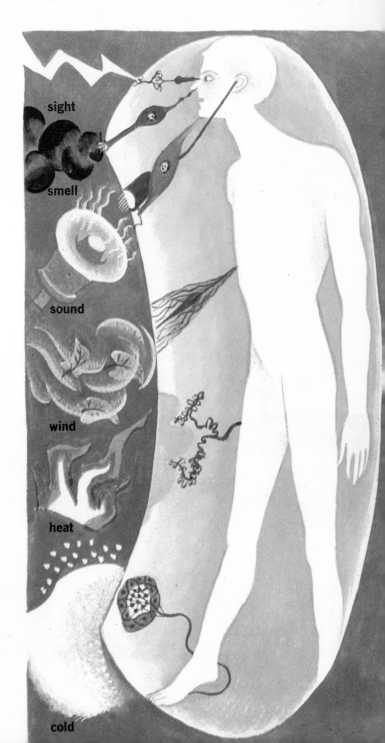

sight

smell

sound

wind

heat

cold

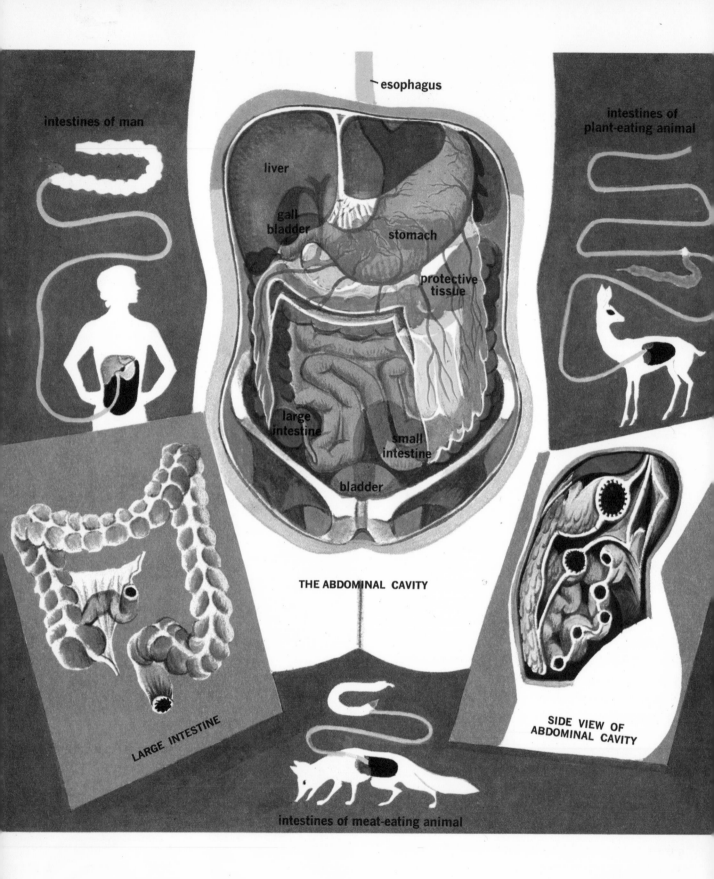

esophagus

intestines of man

liver

gall
bladder

stomach

protective
tissue

large
intestine

small
intestine

bladder

THE ABDOMINAL CAVITY

intestines of
plant-eating animal

SIDE VIEW OF
ABDOMINAL CAVITY

LARGE INTESTINE

intestines of meat-eating animal

Food from the mouth goes down the esophagus into the stomach. The stomach continues the work that started in the mouth—breaking chunks of solid matter into the liquids that the body cells can use as food. Secretions from the stomach wall and from organs such as the liver *help this activity. In the small intestine, the nutritive solid matter is removed and distributed throughout the body by the blood and lymph. In the large intestine, the nutritive liquids are removed and sent to the body's cells. The rest is waste and is excreted.*

64

The Digestive System

THE CELLS that lie within the human body are made up mostly of liquid and can feed only upon liquids. To provide them with the nourishment they need, the body must convert the bulky foods we eat into a smooth, liquid paste. The body must then separate from this paste the tiny particles on which the cells can feed, and dispose of the waste that is left.

The group of organs that break bulky food into particles and separate the nourishing particles from the waste matter are called the digestive organs. Together they form the digestive system.

The system consists of the gastrointestinal tract —mouth, esophagus, stomach, and intestines— and several glands such as the liver, pancreas, and salivary glands, which provide fluids that help break up the food.

All the parts of the intestinal tract below the mouth have muscular tubes that contract and relax, and so push food along to the next stage. The method of moving food in this manner is called peristalsis. It is perhaps best compared to squeezing toothpaste from a tube.

Another type of squeezing takes place in the stomach and small intestine. This motion is called churning. It does not force food along the tube, but simply mixes it up to allow for more thorough digestion.

The first part of the digestive system's job is the conversion of solid food to semi-liquid form. To do this, the body works on the same principle as a group of men breaking up large rocks with heavy hammers. As the rocks are being hammered by some of the men, water is poured on them by others. Slowly the rocks become stones, then gravel, and finally soft, wet dirt.

The hammers of the digestive system are in the mouth. When food first enters the body, it is ripped, crushed, and torn by the teeth. The tongue, which is a powerful muscle, mixes and turns the food so that the teeth can break it up. At the same time, special glands in the mouth moisten the food with saliva to soften it. Saliva also starts the breaking down of certain types of food.

When the food has become soft enough, the tongue pushes it to the back of the mouth and into the throat. There, rings of muscle force it down the esophagus or upper digestive tube.

The esophagus extends almost straight down from the middle of the neck to the bottom of the chest. It is lined with strong muscles that squeeze progressively to make sure that the food is moved in the right direction. Because of these muscles, food would continue moving toward the stomach even if the eater were standing on his head.

The esophagus is simply a passage that connects the mouth and the stomach. It has no di-

The front teeth are designed for tearing; the back teeth for grinding. The tongue, acting as a lever, helps push the chunks of food toward the stomach.

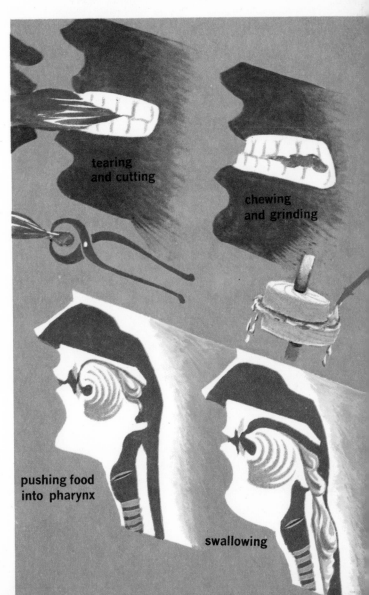

tearing and cutting

chewing and grinding

pushing food into pharynx

swallowing

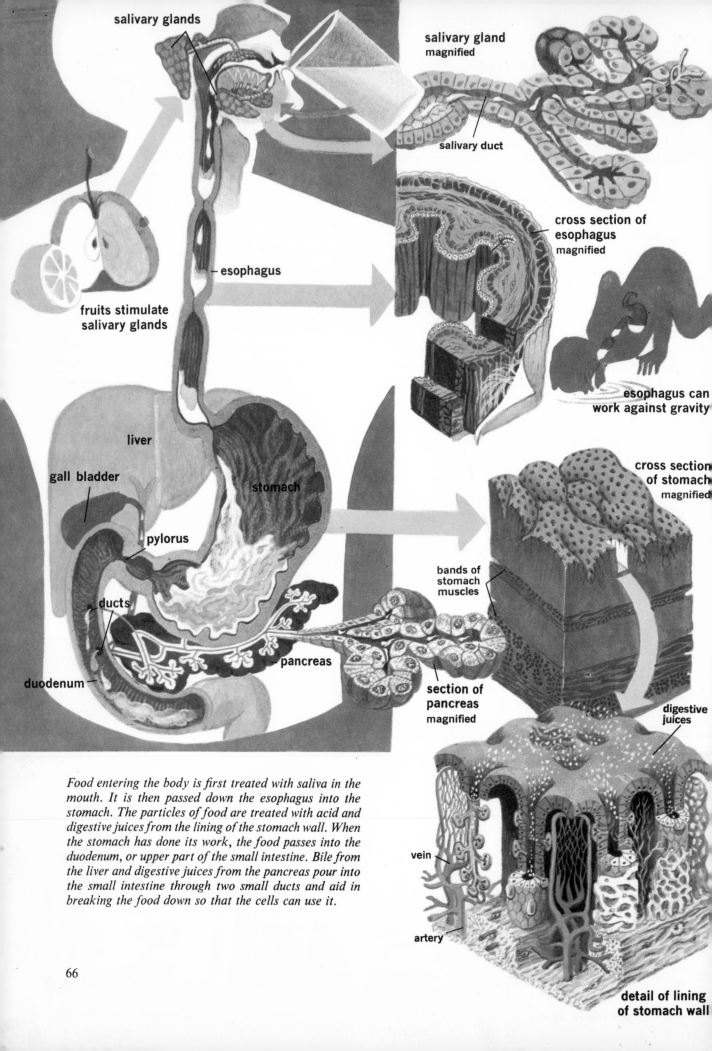

salivary glands

salivary gland
magnified

salivary duct

cross section of
esophagus
magnified

esophagus can
work against gravity

— esophagus

fruits stimulate
salivary glands

liver

gall bladder

stomach

pylorus

ducts

pancreas

duodenum

cross section
of stomach
magnified

bands of
stomach
muscles

section of
pancreas
magnified

digestive
juices

vein

artery

detail of lining
of stomach wall

Food entering the body is first treated with saliva in the mouth. It is then passed down the esophagus into the stomach. The particles of food are treated with acid and digestive juices from the lining of the stomach wall. When the stomach has done its work, the food passes into the duodenum, or upper part of the small intestine. Bile from the liver and digestive juices from the pancreas pour into the small intestine through two small ducts and aid in breaking the food down so that the cells can use it.

66

gestive functions of its own. The stomach, on the other hand, has several special functions.

The stomach is a muscular, elastic pouch that changes its shape depending upon what is in it. Before a meal it may look somewhat like a sausage. Immediately after a Thanksgiving Day dinner, it can look almost like a football.

Because food enters it in semi-liquid form, the stomach needs no grinders or crushers like the teeth. Instead, it is lined with powerful muscles that mash and mix the food into a still finer paste. While the stomach is mixing the food, special cells in its walls release acids and fluids called enzymes that continue the job of breaking down food into the forms that can be fed to the cells.

Just as food is pushed into the esophagus by the tongue when the teeth have broken it into small enough pieces, so it is forced by the stomach into the intestine when the stomach juices have done their work. Special muscles in the stomach move the partly digested food along and pass it through an opening called the pylorus, which connects with the top of the small intestine.

The small intestine is a narrow tube about twenty feet long. To allow it to fit into the space between the diaphragm and the end of the trunk, where the legs join the body, it is coiled and twisted. The tube is lined with muscles that squeeze in turn to force the food along its length.

The inside of the small intestine is lined with four or five million tiny, hairlike projections. These projections provide a large surface for the absorption of the food in the intestine. Because they are hairlike, they are called villi, from the Latin word for "tuft of hair." The villi increase the surface area of the small intestine to about five times that of the skin.

As the semi-liquid food passes through the small intestine, almost all the useful solid particles are removed from it. These particles are extracted by the intestine and passed along to the bloodstream to be distributed throughout the body. The rest of the food continues through the small intestine until it reaches the lower end, where it enters the next portion of the digestive system: the large intestine.

The large intestine is wider and heavier than the small intestine, but considerably shorter. It extends up one side of the abdominal cavity, crosses to the other side of the body, then leads down. Its job is to remove the useful liquid portion of the food. The body gets rid of the remaining solid waste matter at the end of the large intestine.

The organs and glands that aid digestion without actually transporting the food are perhaps just as important in breaking down food as the gastrointestinal tract. Among them are the salivary glands. Also included are the liver and pancreas that give forth bile and the pancreatic juices.

Bile is produced in the liver. It is stored in the gall bladder and enters the small intestine during digestion through a small tube or duct called the bile duct. Joining this duct just before it connects with the small intestine is another, leading from the pancreas. Bile and the pancreatic juices are thus able to flow together into the intestine.

A balanced diet is important to good health. One way to insure a balanced diet is to eat a wholesome meal. The picture below gives an idea of some of the foods that might be included in such a meal.

appetizer or soup　　**meat and vegetables**　　**salad**　　**dessert**　　**milk**

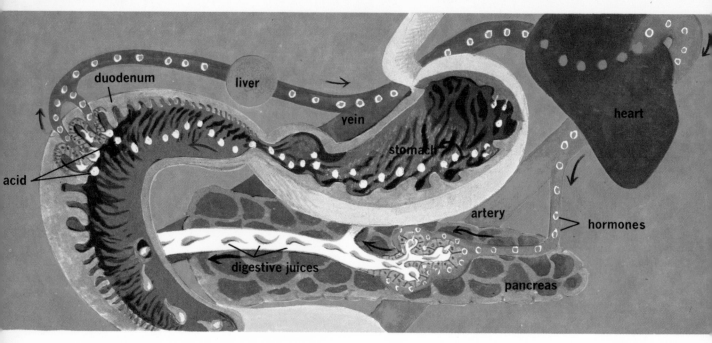

duodenum

liver

acid

vein

stomach

heart

artery

hormones

digestive juices

pancreas

Digestive juices must be given off both in the proper amount and at the right time. Hormones help do this. When acid from the stomach enters the small intestine, a hormone goes into the bloodstream. The hormone is carried to the pancreas and causes it to secrete digestive juices.

Almost all the functions of digestion, except putting food in our mouths and chewing it, are carried on without our having to stop and think about them. These functions are controlled by the automatic nervous system in response to impulses received from the lower part of the brain and the lower spinal cord. Hormones secreted by the digestive organs themselves also help control digestion.

The automatic nervous system works in a highly complex manner. Although it carries out its job pretty much without our knowing about it, there are times when it is influenced by things we see, hear, or feel. Some people, for example, suffer from stomach cramps when they worry. This is an example of how a state of mind can affect an organ that is usually under automatic control. And if the mind can influence the stomach, it seems only reasonable that the stomach should be able to influence the mind. It does, when we feel the sensation of hunger.

Hunger is felt in two ways. First there is a general feeling of weakness, and the body becomes restless and nervous. Scientists do not yet know why this is so.

The second way that hunger is felt is characterized by a feeling of tension, accompanied by cramps in the pit of the stomach. This feeling is caused by contraction of the stomach muscles. When the stomach is empty, and the body is in need of food, the stomach muscles squeeze in and out. These contractions usually continue for about half an hour. Then there is a period lasting from half an hour to two hours when there are no cramps, after which they start again. Of course, most people do not feel the second period of cramps, for they eat when they feel hungry.

Hunger is a *need* for food and is different from appetite which is a *desire* for food. The two usually occur together, but not always. For example, the sight of a piece of cake can often stimulate the desire to eat even though hunger has already been satisfied by a large meal.

A characteristic that the various parts of the digestive system have in common is that they are all lined with smooth membranous tissue. This tissue looks and feels different in different parts of the system, depending upon the function of the part. Underneath the membrane lie various glands. Some of these glands, as in the stomach and intestines, secrete digestive juices. Others provide mucus to lubricate the passage of food.

Sensations of pain that seem to arise from the

digestive organs usually come from the membranes. The organs themselves are capable of feeling only limited pain. Cutting them, for instance, is hardly felt. If the stomach or intestine is swollen with gas, or is twisted or obstructed, pain may be more acute.

One kind of pain that seems to come from a digestive organ is the pain felt in appendicitis. This is caused by an inflammation of the appendix and is felt by the membrane, not by the appendix itself.

"Appendix" means "something attached to or hanging from something else." The body's appendix hangs from one end of the large intestine. It has the form of a small, finger-shaped pouch with an opening at one end. Sometimes bits of food get into it and irritate its membrane until the appendix becomes inflamed and swollen. If the

inflammation is serious enough, the appendix must be removed.

The removal of the appendix has no effect upon man's digestive processes. The appendix is thought to have been of use to primitive man, but in modern times has served no function. In some of the lower animals, however, it is still useful. Rabbits, for example, have a fairly well developed appendix. Rabbits eat considerable bark, and the appendix aids in the digestion of cellulose, which is in bark and wood.

The appendix is often called a vestigial remnant. A vestigial remnant is a structure that is present in the body but that is undeveloped and has lost whatever purpose it once served. Another vestigial remnant in man is the muscle in the ear. If this muscle were developed, man would be able to move his ears around as dogs can.

In the fingerlike villi of the small intestine, the nutritive parts of food are taken in by the lymph vessels to be distributed throughout the body. The intestinal tube is capable of two kinds of motions. One mixes the food, the other pushes it along through the intestine.

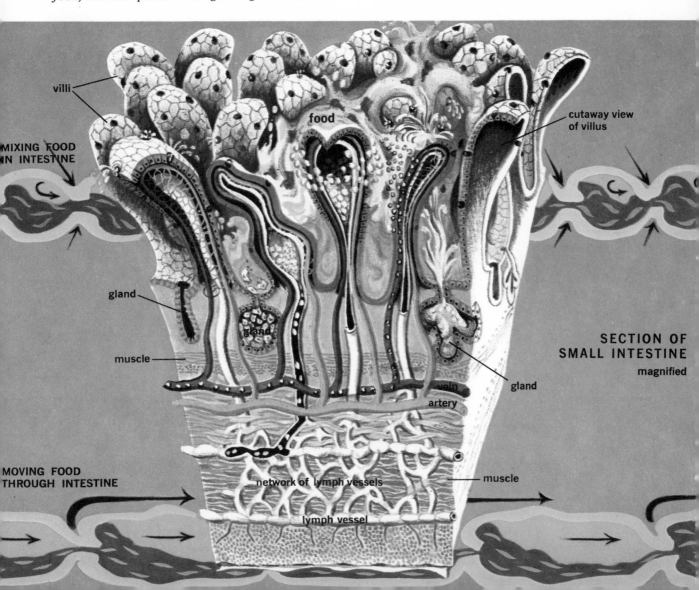

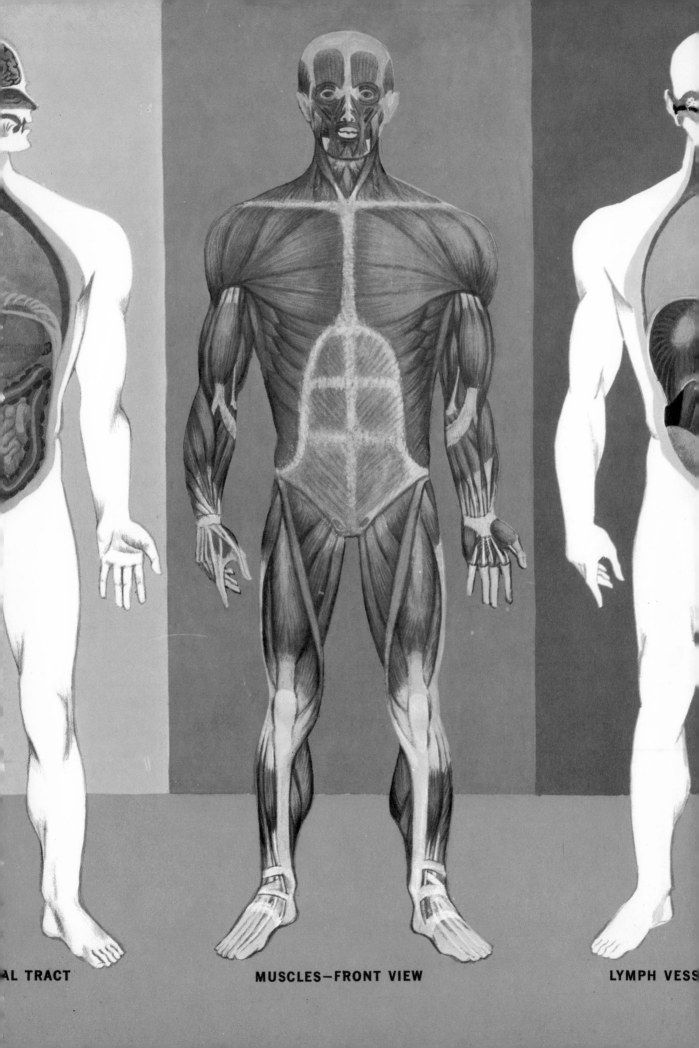

AL TRACT   MUSCLES—FRONT VIEW   LYMPH VESS

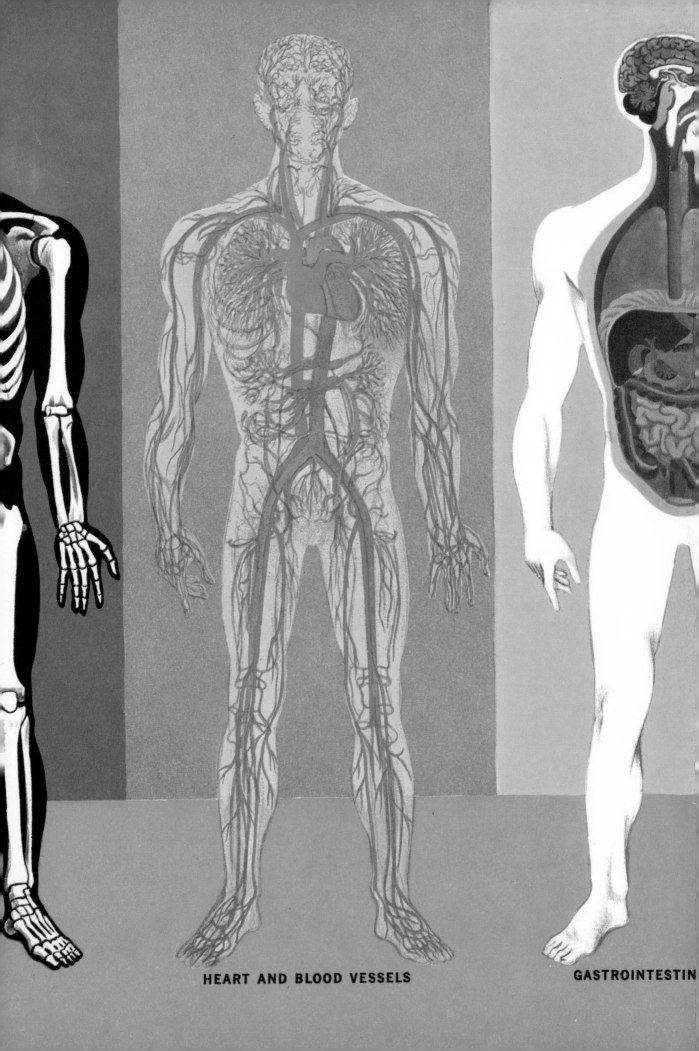

HEART AND BLOOD VESSELS   GASTROINTESTIN

The Body's Hidden Cooks

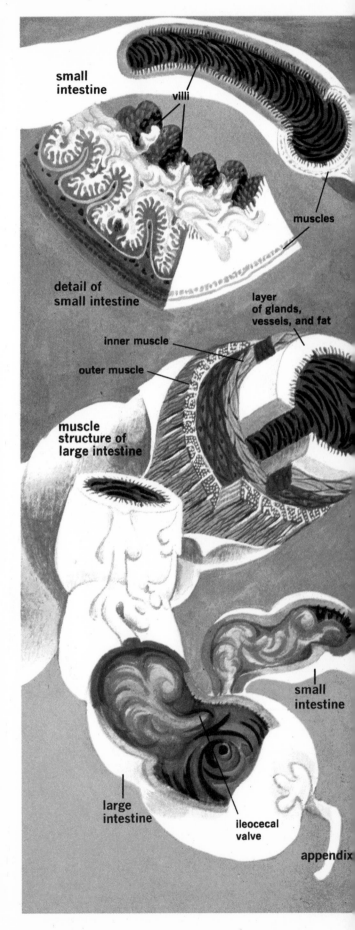

small intestine

villi

muscles

detail of small intestine

layer of glands, vessels, and fat

inner muscle

outer muscle

muscle structure of large intestine

small intestine

large intestine

ileocecal valve

appendix

ACCORDING to the dictionary, a cook is "one who prepares food for eating." Food that is fed to the body's cells, however, might be considered as having been cooked twice—once in the kitchen to serve on the table, and once in the body to prepare it for the cells. The second "cooking" breaks food into tiny particles that the cells can feed upon. These tiny particles are so small that they cannot be seen even under the most powerful microscopes. Such particles are called molecules.

The hidden "cooks" that prepare the food in the body are the digestive juices and enzymes. The materials they work on are the fats, carbohydrates, and proteins in the food we eat.

The digestive juices and enzymes are manufactured in the body's glands and organs and are released when they are needed. If the food that is served to a person has an appealing taste and aroma, the nerves of taste and smell send impulses to the brain passing on this information. The brain then orders the digestive organs to prepare for action. Not all the digestive juices are controlled by the nerves, however. Some are controlled chemically. Certain juices or enzymes that are released in one part of the system, for instance, start a reaction that releases other juices in the next part.

The first digestive juice is released in the mouth. It is saliva, which contains an enzyme called amylase. The body is unable to make use of starch, but it can use certain sugars, even though both of these are carbohydrates. Amylase starts breaking down starch into a sugar the body can use.

The next stage of preparation begins a few minutes later in the stomach and goes on for over an hour. Special cells in the stomach's walls pour

The small intestine of an adult is a muscular tube roughly half an inch in diameter and twenty-two feet long. It is lined with tiny, fingerlike projections called villi. It connects with the large intestine by the ileocecal valve. The large intestine is shorter and wider than the small one, being about five feet long and up to three inches across.

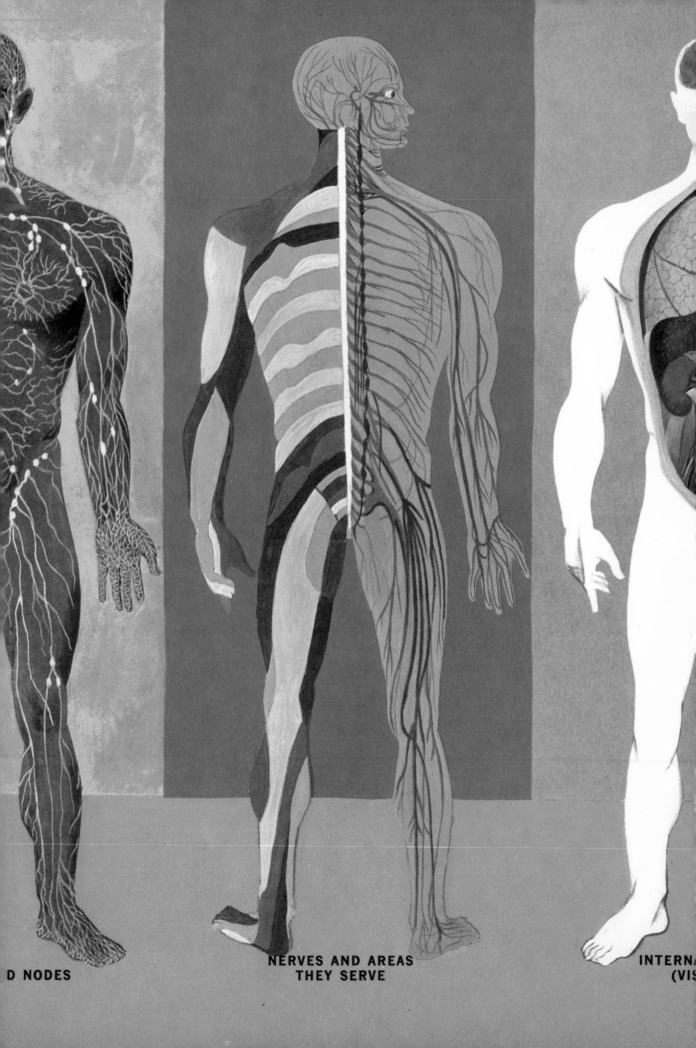

D NODES

NERVES AND AREAS
THEY SERVE

INTERN
(VIS

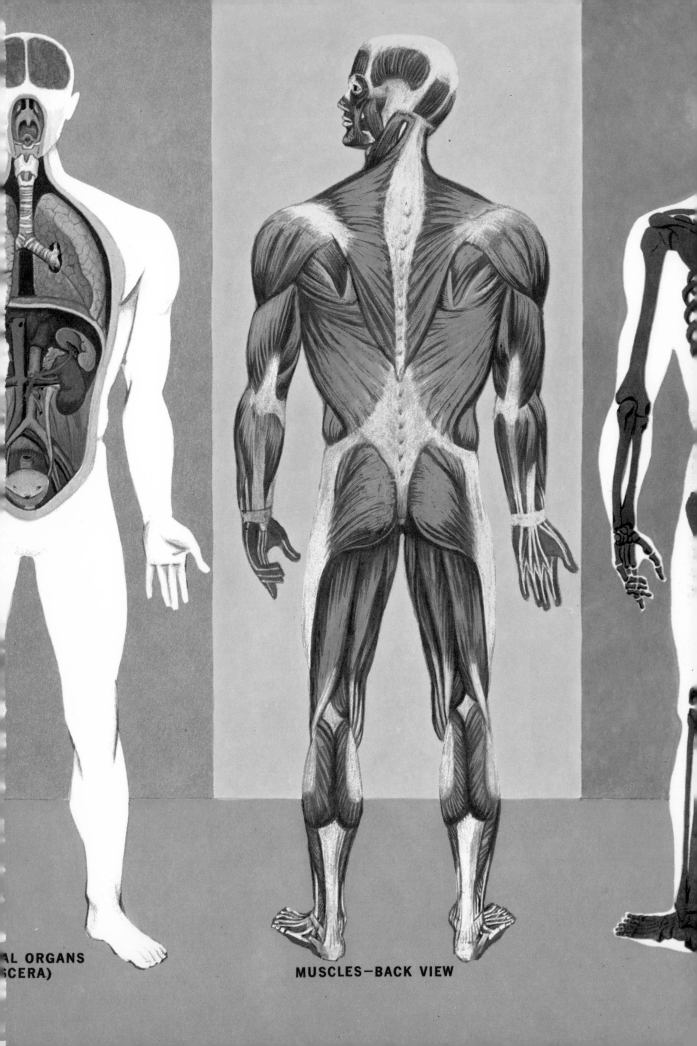

AL ORGANS
CERA)

MUSCLES—BACK VIEW

FOLD BACK

Views of the different systems
and parts of the human body

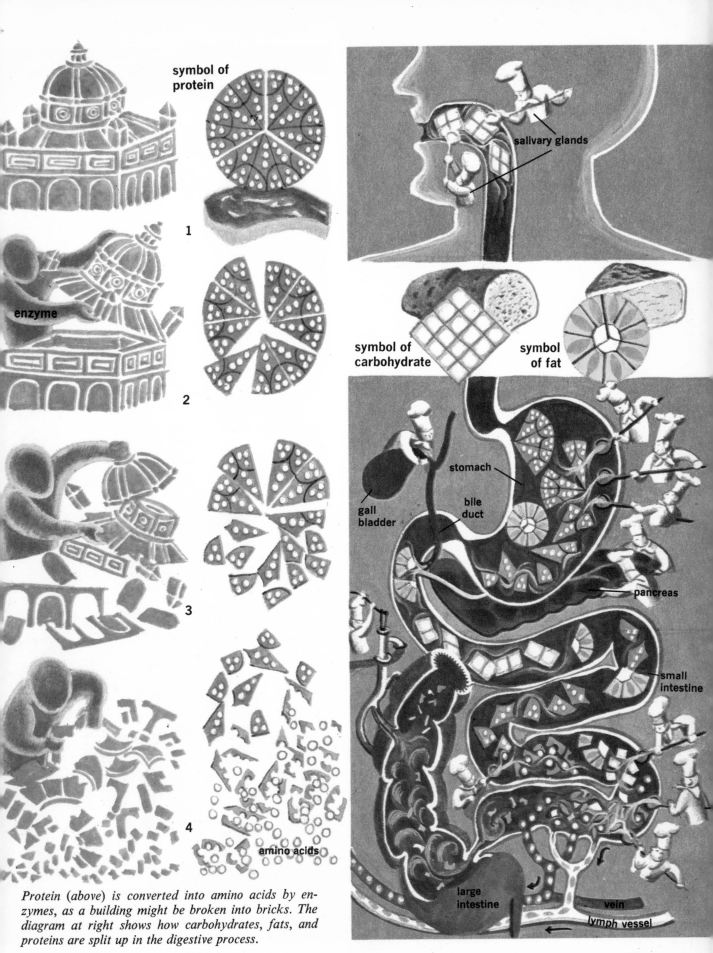

symbol of protein

1

enzyme

2

3

4

amino acids

Protein (above) is converted into amino acids by enzymes, as a building might be broken into bricks. The diagram at right shows how carbohydrates, fats, and proteins are split up in the digestive process.

salivary glands

symbol of carbohydrate

symbol of fat

stomach

gall bladder

bile duct

pancreas

small intestine

large intestine

vein

lymph vessel

a little acid on the food. The acid has effect upon meat, fish, cheese, and similar foods. It also helps another digestive juice—pepsin—to change proteins into amino acids.

The stomach also pours forth another substance, mucin. Mucin coats the wall of the stomach and protects it from the digestive action of acid and pepsin.

Special glands in the stomach give forth all these juices as needed. Such glands work somewhat like faucets that go on and off according to the amount of material there is to be digested.

The food that leaves the stomach is still only partly ready to be taken in by the cells. The final stages of digestion are carried out in the small intestine by juices from the liver and pancreas. The liver sends bile to help break up fat. The pancreas, a large, beltlike gland lying behind the stomach and the upper part of the intestine, secretes juices that split proteins, carbohydrates, and fat.

Proteins are changed into amino acids. Fats are broken down into fatty acids and glycerin. Starches and sugars become glucose.

If these substances are what the body really needs, why don't human beings stop eating such things as meat, vegetables, starches, and sweets? Why not sit down to a generous helping of amino acid molecules, mixed with some fatty acids and glycerin, and sprinkle the whole with glucose?

The answer is largely that man has become used to these foods. The human body is constructed so it can make use of bulky foods. Man's senses respond to the taste and aroma of well-cooked meals, and this helps start the digestive glands functioning. Plain amino acids have neither the taste nor aroma to stimulate the glands.

Man's senses make his body's necessary work more fun. And the enjoyment of food actually helps digestion. Digestive glands in the mouth and stomach work better when we are relaxed and happy, and when we find the food pleasing.

Food odors, as from a roast, rise to the center for smell in the brain. This starts a chain reaction over the nerve pathways which stimulates the digestive glands.

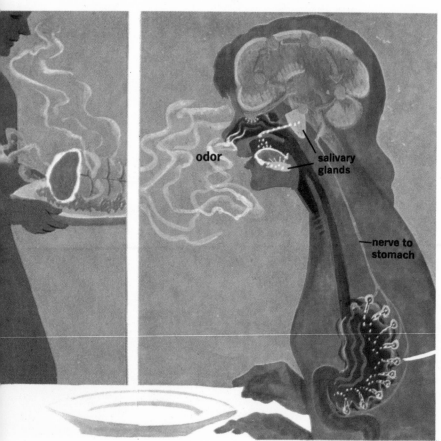

odor

salivary glands

—nerve to stomach

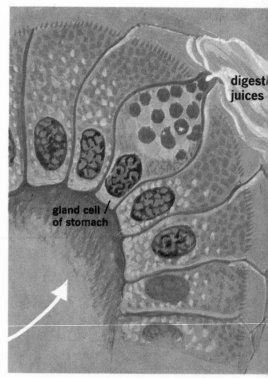

digesti juices

gland cell of stomach

gland cell of stomach is stimulated to release digestive fluid

Sugar, like a candle, can burn—but all burning requires oxygen.

Eating to Do Work

Each cell in the body has two jobs to perform. First, the individual cell—whether in muscle, bone, nerve, or skin tissue—must do its special work toward keeping the body alive. Second, it must keep itself alive, or replace itself if it becomes worn out. Cells of muscle tissue, for example, must tighten up and relax as part of any muscle movement. Cells of muscle tissue must also repair any damage done to them and, by the process called healing, reproduce new cells to replace injured tissue.

To do their work, cells need an important group of foods called carbohydrates. These are substances made up of hydrogen, oxygen, and carbon in a wide variety of combinations. Each different combination is a different substance. Sugar is one; starch is another.

Carbohydrates are found in vegetables, fruits, milk, and foods from grains—such as oatmeal, bread, cake, and rice. They also constitute a large part of candy, syrup, honey, and ordinary sugar. The most important role of carbohydrates is to provide energy for muscle contraction and for the functioning of nerve and brain cells. Carbohydrates are stored chiefly in the liver and muscles.

Scientists measure the exact amount of energy we get from different foods in units called calories.

A tablespoon of honey contains about 100 calories. Pure carbohydrate gives 120 calories for each ounce—but of course, few foods are pure carbohydrate. They are almost always mixtures of salts and water, often fat and protein, and a certain amount of indigestible stuff with no food value at all.

Scientists have figured out how much food, or energy-producing material, we must take in to do the normal work of living without losing weight. A one-year-old child needs 44 calories per day for every pound he weighs. A person thirty to fifty years of age needs only about one-third as many. But a person doing heavy physical work may require 30 calories per pound. These figures are for an average man weighing 150 pounds. For people who are heavier or lighter, and for women, the figures are slightly different.

As a general rule, a man of average weight needs anywhere from 1800 to 4500 calories a day, depending on how much work he does.

The body converts all carbohydrates to a simple sugar. Actually, there are many different kinds of sugars, and all are similar in structure except that some have bigger and more complicated molecules than others. The simplest form is called glucose.

The cells convert sugar into the energy to do

work in much the same way that an automobile engine converts gasoline into energy to turn wheels. Sugar is converted into energy by burning. The oxygen that comes into the body through breathing is used for this burning process, although sugar can sometimes be used in the body even without oxygen.

"Burning" the sugar does not involve a blazing fire and clouds of smoke, as when wood is burned.

Rather, it is a less spectacular kind of chemical reaction in which the heat is produced at a low and steady rate.

To illustrate how sugar can burn, take a lump of sugar and dip one corner into cigarette ash so that some of the ash clings to the sugar. Hold a lighted match to the corner. After a few seconds, the sugar will begin to burn with a small, pale blue flame.

The foods fed to the body provide the energy needed to keep the human machine running. Some of these foods are burned immediately, some are stored for later use. Many of the parts of the body perform much the same functions that the parts of an automobile perform, as shown below.

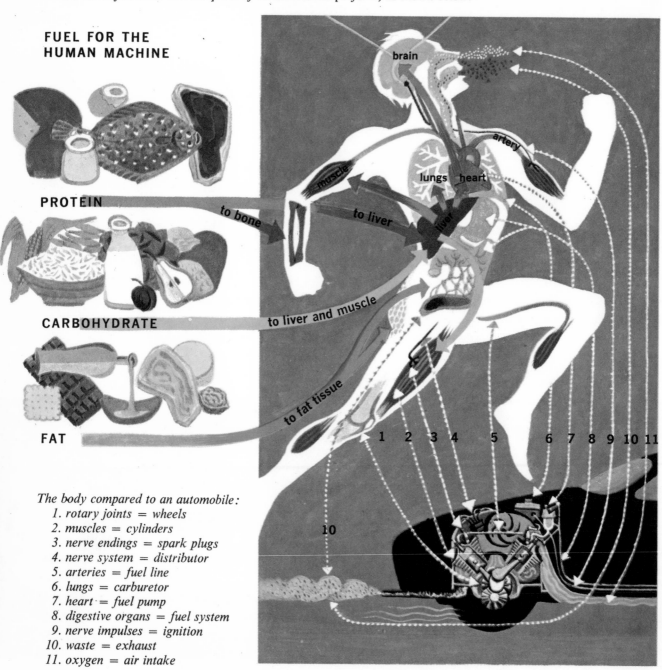

FUEL FOR THE HUMAN MACHINE

PROTEIN

CARBOHYDRATE

FAT

The body compared to an automobile:
1. *rotary joints = wheels*
2. *muscles = cylinders*
3. *nerve endings = spark plugs*
4. *nerve system = distributor*
5. *arteries = fuel line*
6. *lungs = carburetor*
7. *heart = fuel pump*
8. *digestive organs = fuel system*
9. *nerve impulses = ignition*
10. *waste = exhaust*
11. *oxygen = air intake*

To show how important oxygen is to burning, take a small candle and light it. Let the wax drip for a moment into a shallow dish so that the candle will stand up in the soft wax. Pour a little water into the dish and place a large glass jar, mouth down, over the candle. The water in the dish will prevent any air from passing into or out of the jar. Within a few seconds after the jar is put in place, the flame will grow dim and then go out. This is because all the oxygen in the air inside the jar has been burned up.

In the cells, glucose is slowly burned—or oxidized—into three substances: water, carbon dioxide, and special, energy-rich materials.

Sugar is burned by the body as it is taken in, but there is another important class of food that the body stores up: fat. Some of the fat we eat is soon burned in the body to produce energy. Some fat is continually being stored. But fats such as meat fat, milk fat, and oil must be broken down and converted into body fat before they can be stored. Once stored, fat can be removed and burned to fill the body's energy requirements. Only a very short time is required to change food fat to body fat. Thus body fat is constantly being formed and broken down.

Imagine a warehouse in which boxes are delivered at every door at the same time, and from which boxes are also being removed. Some of the boxes taken away may have been delivered only a few minutes earlier, while some may have been there for weeks. In the same way, fat tissue that is being burned in the body this minute may have been stored just last week—or months ago.

Once the body stops eating, it begins to live on its fat. There are special places where the body stores fat, and there is fatty tissue in every organ except the brain. The fat storage depots are located in different places in the body, ready to make delivery whenever necessary.

Fat actually gives about twice as much energy for each ounce that is stored as carbohydrates do. Fat comes from butter, cream, and other milk products such as cheese, and from the fatty parts of meat and nuts. There is even some fat in vegetables.

Fat has several other functions besides being the body's major source of energy. The main fat storage depots lie in sheets under the skin. They provide us with an insulating blanket that helps keep us warm in cold weather. The fat around joints and nerves, and between muscle fibers, acts as a cushion against injury when we bump into something. Fat also helps to hold up and anchor certain organs, such as the kidneys, in their proper positions in the body. The only places where there is no fat is in the brain and other parts of the central nervous system. However, nerve and brain tissue are composed of substances very similar to fat.

The number of calories the body needs depends upon what it is doing. Even at rest the body needs fuel. The diagram below shows how many calories an adult might need for various activities.

USING CALORIES

sleep
1800 calories

digestion
2100 calories

rest
2500 calories

light work
3300 calories

heavy work
up to 4500 calories

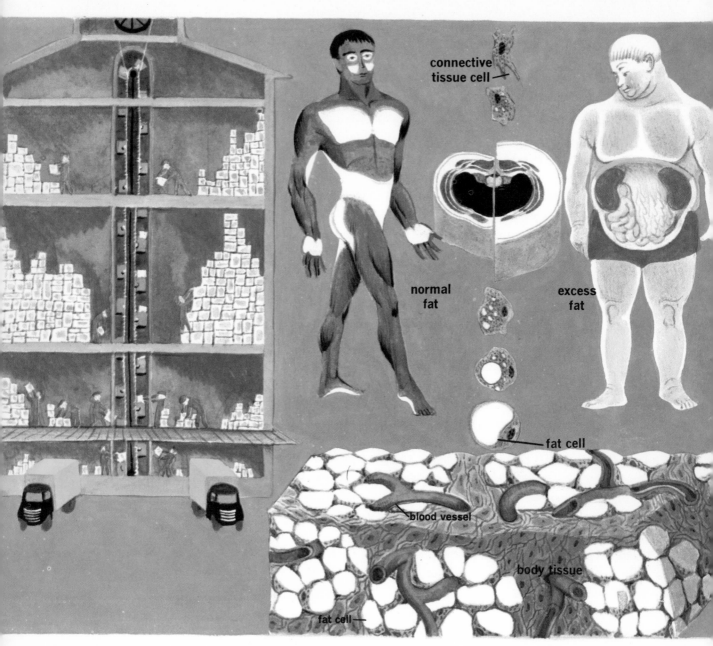

The cells of the body store fat much as a warehouse stores goods. Connective tissue cells, like rooms in a warehouse, receive and give off fat as needed. If the same amount of fat is burned as is taken in, fat deposits are normal. If more is taken in than is burned, the body is overweight.

An interesting thing about fat is that it can be formed from carbohydrate and protein. Fat can therefore form on a diet free from milk or cream or other fat-containing substances. Eating sugar and protein, such as meat, with most of the fat removed will add weight just as fat will. Of course more protein and carbohydrate would be needed if a person were to gain weight, because these food substances are not so rich as fat.

The third important substance in food is protein. This comes mostly from meat, fish, milk products, and eggs, but fruits and vegetables also contain some of it. In the stomach and intestine, protein is broken down into amino acids—the basic units of which protein is composed. They pass into the bloodstream and go to the liver where they are broken down still further. Finally the fragments are used to build new body proteins to replace worn-out tissues in many organs. These proteins also form important parts of the blood, of the lymph fluid, and of enzymes. Protein can also, in part, be converted to carbohydrate.

Vitamins

THE BODY needs fairly large quantities of carbo-hydrates, proteins, and fats. One type of nutrient, however, is needed in only minute amounts. A pinhead would hold all that is needed for a day, yet vitamins are so essential to human life that they are named after life itself. *Vita* is the Latin word for "life."

We will all probably live longer, fuller, healthier lives than people who lived a hundred years ago. We had the good luck to be born in the mid-twentieth century, rather than in the days when nothing at all was known about vitamins. In those days the lack of vitamins caused serious diseases. Today, such diseases can be cleared up at the first symptoms by the addition of the proper vitamin to the diet. Many different vitamins have already been identified; four of these are known to be particularly important to the human body.

Vitamin A is manufactured by the body from plants such as carrots and other yellow vegetables, spinach, broccoli, and beet greens. It is also found in the livers of codfish and halibut as well as other fish and animals, and in butter, eggs, and cheese. A diet deficient in foods containing vitamin A has a harmful effect upon the eyes and eyelids, some-times leading to severe infections.

One of the symptoms of a lack of vitamin A is a condition called night blindness. People suffering from this have difficulty seeing in a dim light. Their skin may also be rough and dry and scaly. It was once thought that a lack of vitamin A made people more susceptible to colds. It is now known, however, that a person with a diet rich in vitamin A can catch a cold as easily as anyone else, and will not be helped by increased doses of the vitamin.

Since so many of the foods we eat contain either plenty of vitamin A or the substance from which vitamin A is made, severe deficiencies seldom occur in this part of the world. Nevertheless anyone who does not like vegetables, butter, eggs, or cheese might possibly get too little vitamin A. This is one reason why it is so important to have a prop-erly balanced diet.

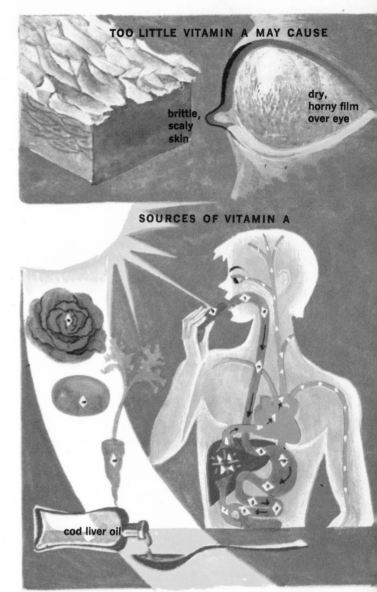

Vitamin A is essential to good health. Green and yellow vegetables, cheeses, and oils are all good sources of sup-ply for this vitamin.

Vitamin A can be stored in the body for long periods of time. As with fish and other animals, it is stored in our livers. Because of our ability to retain vitamin A, the symptoms of a deficiency do not appear until quite a long time after we have stopped receiving enough of the vitamin. This is quite different from some of the other vitamins, particularly vitamin C, which the body can scarcely store at all and which must be supplied to it constantly.

Vitamin B is really a collection of twelve sub-stances more properly called vitamin B complex. All have in common the fact that they can be dissolved in water, and all are found in liver and

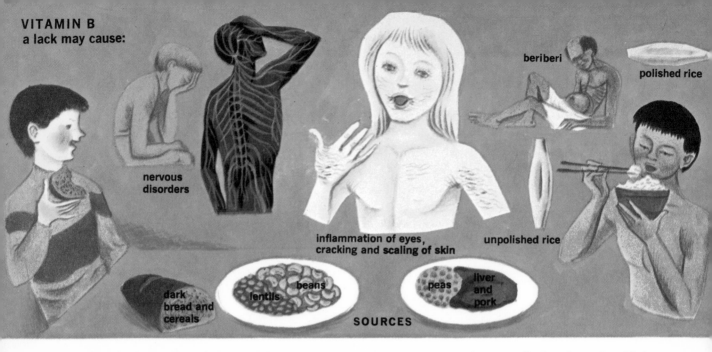

nervous disorders

beriberi

polished rice

inflammation of eyes, cracking and scaling of skin

unpolished rice

dark bread and cereals

lentils

beans

peas

liver and pork

SOURCES

Vitamin B actually includes ten different substances—the vitamin B complex—usually found together. The body stores little vitamin B, so a lack of it in the diet shows up in a few weeks.

yeast. The function of some of these materials is still a mystery, but we do know a good deal about three or four of them. In fact, vitamin B_1 was the earliest vitamin to be discovered. It helped give rise to the idea that a disease could be due to a lack of something in the system.

The discovery of vitamins began in 1897 in Java where a Dutch physician formed the idea that the disease called beriberi might arise from a diet of polished rice, or rice from which the husks had been removed. The people of Java consumed little other than polished rice, and many of them developed paralysis and body swelling, leading, in some instances, to death. By adding the material that had been removed in the polishing process, this doctor found that he could cure the disease.

About fifteen years later another scientist identified the substance in rice husks and coined the term vitamine, since shortened to vitamin, to describe it. It was later discovered that the substance whose lack causes beriberi is only one of the vitamins. This substance is called thiamine or vitamin B_1. It is essential to the normal functioning of the nerves and the heart.

Vitamin B_2, or riboflavin, is another important member of the B-complex group. A lack of it causes inflammation of the eyes and soreness of

the tongue and corners of the mouth. A third B vitamin, called niacin, prevents the disease called pellagra; the skin and tongue become sore and the person may suffer from intestinal and mental disturbances. When the relationship between pellagra and mental disorders was discovered, a great many people previously considered insane were cured with niacin.

Folic acid and vitamin B_{12} are important in the formation of red blood cells. Anemia is caused by insufficient amounts of them.

The best sources of the B vitamins are whole grains, peas, beans, beef, pork, liver, yeast, and nuts. Eggs, fish, milk, and many vegetables contain moderate amounts of these vitamins. Since cooking

depression

bleeding of the gums and mucus membrane

People who are lazy and grumpy may not be getting enough vitamin C and should eat more fresh fruit.

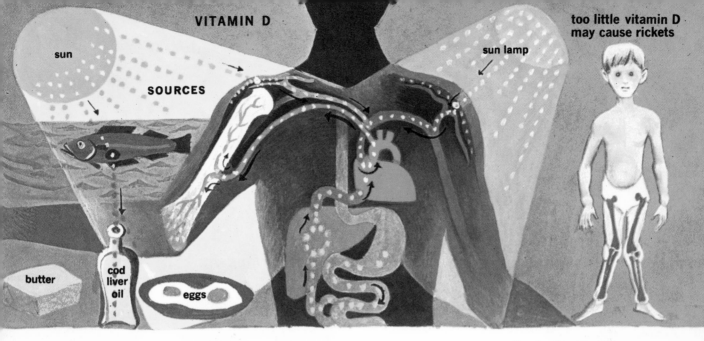

VITAMIN D

too little vitamin D
may cause rickets

sun

SOURCES

sun lamp

butter

cod
liver
oil

eggs

With the help of sunlight, the body can make its own vitamin D from a substance found in the skin. Lacking vitamin D, the body fails to absorb enough calcium and phosphorus for bones to form properly.

may destroy some of the vitamin B group, it is advisable to eat some of the foods containing vitamin B without cooking them.

Vitamin C is necessary to the small blood vessels. Without it, the disease called scurvy occurs. The blood vessels become fragile and are easily broken. In infants and children, bones may also become deformed. Vitamin C is found in oranges, lemons, grapefruit, tomatoes, green vegetables, and potatoes. Until a little over a hundred years ago, scurvy was one of the great perils of long sea voyages, because sailors were unable to get fresh fruits or vegetables. Finally the English navy had every ship carry lemons or limes. Sailors of other nations laughed and called the English sailors "limeys"—

but the "limeys" did not come down with scurvy.

Vitamin D is important to bone formation and to bone health. Without it, bones become soft and weak, so that they bend too easily under strain. Vitamin D can be manufactured by the body itself when there is plenty of sunshine, and it can be taken in from the livers of fish or animals, and from egg yolks. The body needs very little vitamin D, but that little bit makes all the difference in the world.

The story of vitamin D began early in the nineteenth century when a Polish doctor found that by exposing children to strong sunlight the softening and deformity of bones that is known as rickets could be cured or prevented. Later, an Englishman wrote to missionaries all over the world and discovered that in places with plenty of sunlight rickets never occurred regardless of how bad living conditions were. Finally, shortly after World War I, it was discovered that "artificial sun," as ultra-violet rays were then called, could cure rickets. This is because vitamin D is formed by the action of ultra-violet rays on the skin. It can also be taken by mouth.

The vitamin itself was not discovered until 1922, when it was found in cod liver oil. Most doctors today prescribe vitamin D for young children. In addition, dairy companies now add the vitamin to milk so that everybody who drinks milk has at least part of his needs supplied.

SOURCES

citrus
fruits

tomatoes

sauerkraut

85

some foods that
contain carbohydrate are:
corn
peas
beans
potatoes
honey
fruits
whole-grain breads
cereals

CARBOHYDRATE   provides fuel an

some foods that
contain fat are:
dairy products
meat
olive oil
ice cream

FAT   provides body wit

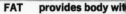

some foods that
contain protein are:
dairy products
peas
poultry
fish
red meat
liver
beans
nuts

PROTEIN   contains nitroge

some foods that contain
the mineral calcium are:
dairy products
green leafy vegetables
yellow vegetables
fruits

some foods that contain
the mineral phosphorus are:
dairy products
lean meat
shellfish
poultry
whole grain cereals

some foods that contain
the mineral iron are:
liver
red meat
greens
nuts
dried fruits
cereals

some foods that contain
the mineral iodine are:
iodized salt
salt-water fish

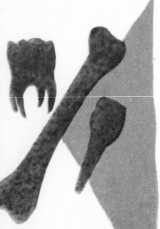

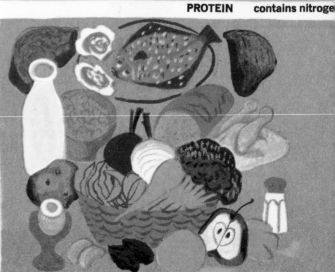

MINERALS   build strong teeth

...ASSES OF FOODS ON THE BODY

...main source of quick energy for the body

...eets of insulation and storage of energy

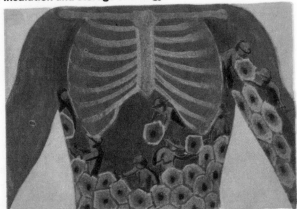

...hich helps make and repair body tissues

...and bones; help regulate activity of thyroid gland

Eating to Grow

IN ONE WAY OR ANOTHER, all the creatures of the earth are related. Not only are all creatures related to one another, but it could be said that all living creatures, all plants, and even the earth itself are related. All are composed mostly of the same building blocks. These building blocks are oxygen, hydrogen, carbon, and nitrogen.

Every cell in the body needs a generous supply of oxygen in order to stay alive. The heart and lungs work together to take oxygen from the air and convey it to the bloodstream, where the red blood cells take it to every part of the body. Hydrogen and carbon enter the body mostly in the form of carbohydrates in food. The digestive system takes care of preparing carbohydrates for the body's use.

Nitrogen is perhaps not mentioned so frequently as the other three elements, but it too is essential to life. Without nitrogen, the body tissues would soon wear out. If there were no nitrogen, new cells could not grow to replace those that are old or injured.

Except for red blood cells, each of the billions of cells in the body has its own nucleus. No cell can live without its nucleus. No cell can reproduce itself without a nucleus, for it is the nucleus that divides in half and forms two cells where before there had been only one. The most important substance in any nucleus is a particular kind of protein. Proteins differ from all other food substances because they are the only ones that contain nitrogen. Even hemoglobin, the substance in the red blood cell that carries oxygen to the cells, is a protein.

Oxygen, carbon, hydrogen, and nitrogen are the building blocks of the foods we eat. In varying combinations, they form the fats, carbohydrates, and proteins that provide us with nourishment.

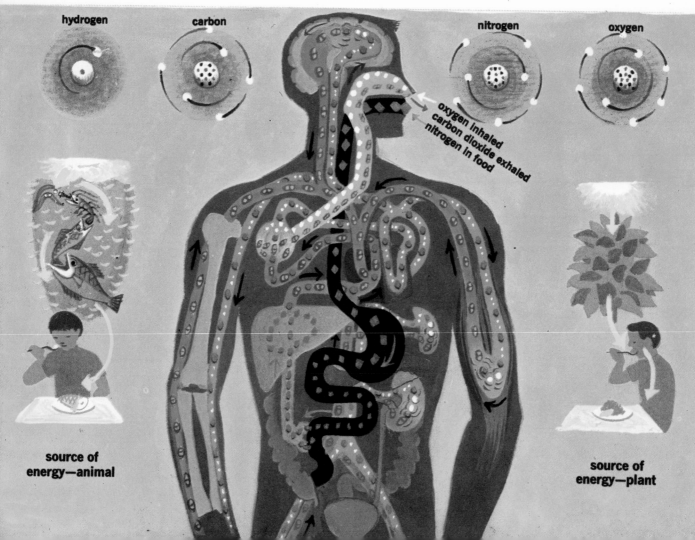

hydrogen   carbon   nitrogen   oxygen

oxygen inhaled
carbon dioxide exhaled
nitrogen in food

source of energy—animal

source of energy—plant

THE CARBON CYCLE

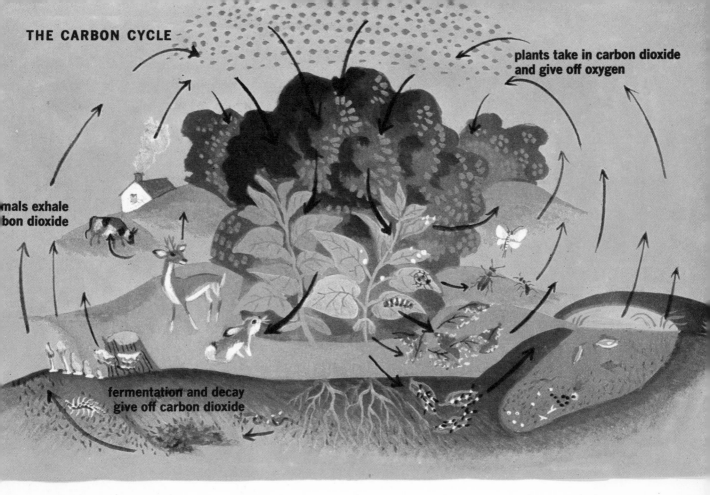

plants take in carbon dioxide and give off oxygen

...mals exhale ...bon dioxide

fermentation and decay give off carbon dioxide

Carbon circulates from the earth to the atmosphere. The carbon dioxide that is breathed out by animals, for example, is taken in by plants which, by a biological process called photosynthesis, convert it to oxygen. Thus there is always enough carbon to supply the world's needs.

Proteins are taken into the body when we eat such foods as meat, fish, chicken, the white of eggs, milk, cheese, and wheat.

Protein is needed daily; it cannot be stored like fat. Tissues must be replaced when there is damage, such as a cut or a bruise, or when there is disease. Even in healthy bodies, tissue all through the body is being worn out and replaced every minute of every day. However, not all tissue can be replaced. The nerve cells in the brain and spinal cord cannot reproduce themselves. This inability to reproduce is true of certain other tissues, too.

All living things need nitrogen. Plants draw it up from the earth through their roots. Some animals get it by eating plants. Their bodies change plant protein to animal protein. Other animals get protein by eating those animals that have already changed the plant protein into animal protein.

All grazing animals such as cows, goats, deer, and sheep are plant eaters. Men eat both plants and the flesh of grazing animals—and fish which have fed on plants that grow in the water. Farmers put extra amounts of nitrogen into the soil to help the growth of plants.

Actually, nitrogen and oxygen move in constant cycles that are of great importance to plant and animal life. Nitrogen makes up four-fifths of the air we breathe but it cannot be used in this form. It passes in and out of the lungs with oxygen. Nitrogen in the air can be used by plants and animals only after certain soil bacteria have converted it into nitrates. These nitrates dissolve in water and are absorbed by the plants.

When animals or plants die, their bodies decay and the nitrogen in them is returned to the earth. There the nitrogen is either used again or it returns to the air from where it originally came. This taking of nitrogen out of the air, using it, and returning it is called the nitrogen cycle.

The oxygen cycle works somewhat similarly. Oxygen is taken from the atmosphere by animals

plankton

nitr

Nitrogen is contained in the air, the ground, and in waste and decayed matter. Plant-eating animals get nitrogen from plants. Other animals receive it through eating plant-eating animals, or marine life such as plankton. Farmers often enrich their fields with nitrates to increase the nitrogen content of their crops.

and combined with carbon to form carbon dioxide. From this, animals are able to produce energy to sustain life. By a biological process called photosynthesis, plants are able to split up carbon dioxide and release pure oxygen which can then be breathed again. If it were not for this, all the oxygen of the air might soon be used up. The ability of plants to produce oxygen from carbon dioxide helps to make life possible on this planet.

In a sense, there is also a carbon cycle. Plants get carbon from carbon dioxide by photosynthesis. Human beings and animals eat the plants and get carbon from them. The animals eventually die and the carbon of their bodies forms carbon dioxide which floats away in the air until it is again taken in by a plant. Then the process is repeated. These cycles give clear examples of how plants and animals help support each other.

plankton

waste and decayed matter

The Magic Harp

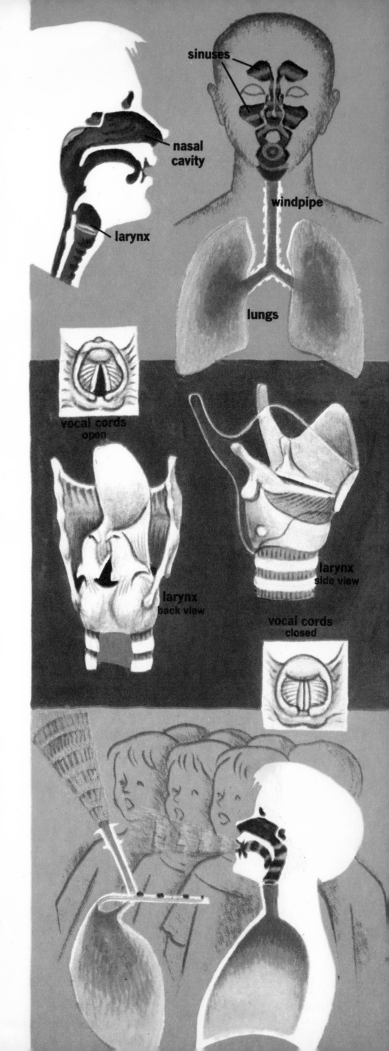

sinuses

nasal cavity

windpipe

larynx

lungs

vocal cords open

larynx back view

larynx side view

vocal cords closed

Listen to the wind!" people sometimes say, but what they hear is the sound of leaves and branches vibrating in the moving air. Long ago, kings who lived in windy castles had strings of different lengths tied side by side. When the breezes blew on them, the strings made beautiful murmuring sounds.

There are many different kinds of wind harps, but the most musical one in the world is the one that sings, talks, laughs, and cries.

Put your fingertips lightly on the front of your throat and hum a song. The steady vibrating you feel under your skin is the harp. The wind that blows through it is your breath coming up from your lungs. The harp is called the larynx, and its strings are called the vocal cords. The larynx is protected by a tough layer of cartilage. Some people call it the Adam's apple.

The throat is a highway for many kinds of traffic. Food that is swallowed passes down the throat on the way to the stomach. In breathing, air passes down the throat on its way to the lungs. In talking, air must come up the throat. But the three kinds of traffic fortunately do not get in each other's way.

The human harp—the larynx—lies in a small cave of muscle in the front of the neck, a little below the back of the tongue. The entrance of this cave is protected from food by a little curtain of cartilage, the epiglottis. The larynx rises up against this curtain to keep out food every time you swallow. With your fingers you can easily feel it move up and down.

Instead of using many different strings to make all the sounds in the human voice, the larynx needs only two little bands of tissue. They are stretched side by side in a V pointing toward the front of the throat. Air from the lungs passes

Air is squeezed from the lungs as it is from a bagpipe. As it passes through the larynx, the vocal cords make the air vibrate and sound is produced. The sinuses and the hollow nasal cavity act as echo chambers, strengthening and amplifying the sound.

between the edges of the two bands and makes them vibrate. This vibrating motion is what makes the sound.

When the edges of the bands are close together in a narrow V, the sound is high. When the space between them is wide, the sound is deep. The pitch of the sound also depends on how tightly or loosely the bands are held by the larynx muscles. Changes in pitch can be made quickly. Human beings are so used to making just the sound they wish that they don't have to think which muscles to use.

When the bands of the larynx are long and thick, all the sounds seem low and deep. This is why men have voices that are much deeper than children's.

No two people's voices are exactly the same. The larynx differs from person to person. One's voice also depends on the shape of the throat and mouth. No two people have exactly the same shape of nose, and no two people have exactly the same kind of throat.

The sounds in speech depend also on our lips, tongue, and teeth—how they are shaped and how we use them.

You forgot long ago how you learned to make the sounds of speech. To understand what difficult things you learned without knowing it, recite to yourself the different letters of the alphabet and notice, as you do so, how many motions of lips, tongue, and throat are needed.

Many animals have some kind of vocal cords, and some birds can utter words, but only human beings can really speak.

The position of the tongue, teeth, and lips is different for each of the sounds we make. This difference can be demonstrated by pronouncing the letters shown in the illustrations above and below.

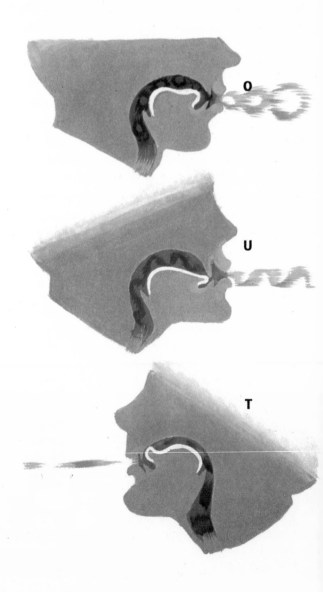

Take a Deep Breath

LONG, long ago, before men knew anything at all about the human body, they knew that breathing is connected with life. "The breath of life" is a saying that is found in the most ancient languages we know. Not until fairly recent times, however, did men understand *how* breathing is connected with life.

Life depends on breathing because the cells of the body need oxygen, which is one of the gases in the air. We breathe in—inhale—to bring fresh supplies of air to the lungs, which will take the oxygen from it. We breathe out—exhale—to get rid of the other gases in the air that the body doesn't need, as well as waste gases that the body has made while doing work.

Anyone who has watched a steam engine working has seen smoke coming out of the smokestack. Anyone who has watched an automobile running has probably noticed a blue gas coming out of the exhaust pipe at the rear. An automobile engine burns gasoline to make the car move. The blue gas is a waste from that burning—it has to be disposed of, or else the engine will stop. The cells of the human body use oxygen to keep the body alive. The waste is the gas that must be breathed out. It is carbon dioxide.

The separation of oxygen from the air by the lungs is important and delicate work. For this reason the air coming to the lungs must be as clean as possible. The air travels only a short distance—from the nose to the chest. In that short space, the body uses many different ways to clean the dust, dirt, and germs from the air.

Air enters the body through the nostrils. Inside the nose are fine hairs that catch many of the larger dust particles in the air. The inner surface of the nose is lined with a thick layer of fluid to which other dust particles stick. High up in the nose are very fine hairlike projections called cilia that extend from the cells of the membrane lining the nose. These are in constant motion like delicate fans, pushing the dirt back down toward the openings of the nostrils.

The nose is also lined with many fine blood vessels, which warm the air that passes through. On a cold day, the nostrils often feel colder than the throat. This is because the blood vessels of the nose warm the air somewhat before it reaches the throat. When the air is very cold, this heating effect is not enough, and the cold air is apt to make the chest ache.

The back of the nose is just above and behind the back of the mouth. Air and food pass together for a short distance down the throat through a tube which then splits into two separate passages: one for food and the other for air. The epiglottis keeps food out of the passage leading to the lungs. However, particles containing food or other solids sometimes may start toward the lungs. When this happens, we say that food is "going down the

Many machines, like people, breathe. Air enters and is used up. Waste gases, such as the smoke of the locomotive or exhaust of the car, are sent out. The body's waste gas is carbon dioxide.

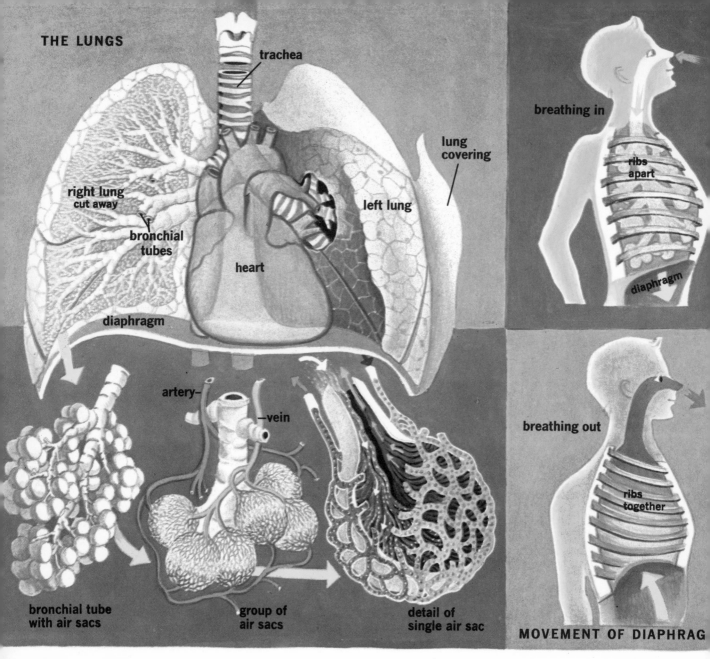

THE LUNGS

trachea

right lung
cut away

bronchial
tubes

left lung

lung
covering

heart

diaphragm

artery—

—vein

bronchial tube
with air sacs

group of
air sacs

detail of
single air sac

breathing in

ribs
apart

diaphragm

breathing out

ribs
together

MOVEMENT OF DIAPHRAG

Inside the lungs are many microscopically small, spongy balls called air sacs. They are covered with tiny blood vessels called capillaries. The air sacs remove carbon dioxide from the blood that flows through the capillaries and in turn supply the blood with fresh oxygen.

wrong way." The body protects its air supply by blowing a short, sharp blast from the lungs. This results in choking and coughing.

The windpipe is a tough muscular tube supported by rings of cartilage which can be felt below the larynx. It, too, is lined with cilia and a fluid that traps germs and other material from the air. The cilia again have the important function of sweeping dust and dirt upward and away from the lungs. However, they are not completely effective—most people's lungs are grayish-black from deposits of coal and dirt breathed in with the air. This material is quite harmless except in certain

types of quarries. To avoid damage to their lungs, workers in such places wear masks.

The windpipe forks into two smaller pipes called bronchi or bronchial tubes. One leads to the right lung, the other to the left. These again branch into smaller and smaller tubes, just as the branches of a tree grow smaller. The smallest branches finally lead into clusters of tiny air sacs that perform the main work of the lungs. Oxygen is taken out of the air and exchanged for carbon dioxide inside these tiny air sacs.

This exchange takes place in tiny blood vessels, or capillaries, in the walls of the alveoli, or air

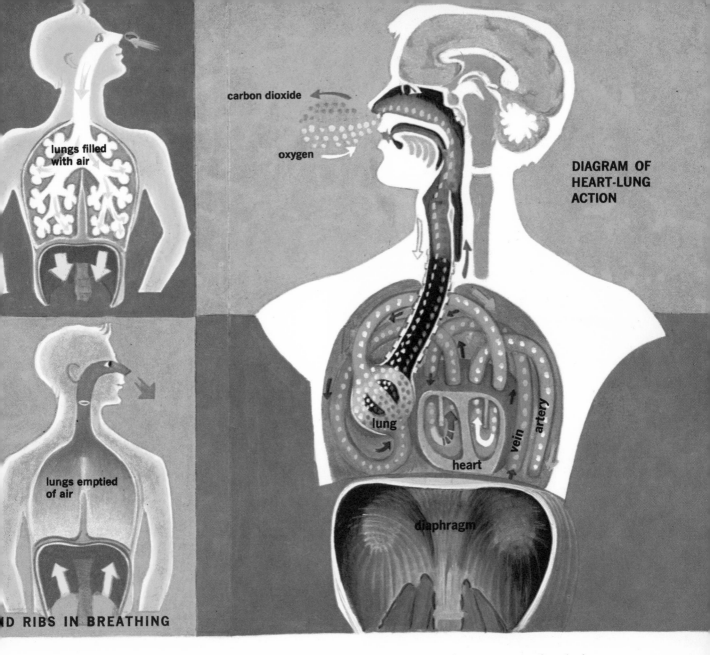

lungs filled
with air

D RIBS IN BREATHING

lungs emptied
of air

carbon dioxide

oxygen

DIAGRAM OF
HEART-LUNG
ACTION

lung

vein

artery

heart

diaphragm

The blood carrying carbon dioxide moves through veins to the heart. From there it is pumped to the lungs where carbon dioxide is given up to the lung sacs and oxygen is taken in. An artery carries the blood back to the heart which then pumps it through other arteries to the rest of the body.

sacs. After the carbon dioxide has passed from the blood through the capillary and alveolar walls, it is breathed out by the lungs. Oxygen breathed into the lungs goes through the alveolar and capillary walls into the bloodstream.

The lungs fit into a boxlike space. The bottom of the box is the sheet of muscle called the diaphragm, and the sides of the box are the ribs and the muscles that move them. When the diaphragm moves down and the ribs spread, the lungs are stretched and air rushes in through the nose and windpipe to fill the extra space. A few seconds later the diaphragm relaxes, the lungs are squeezed

back to their original size, and much of the air is forced out.

Infants breathe 30 to 40 times a minute. By the time a child is six years old, its breathing rate has slowed down to about 22 times a minute. Between the ages of fifteen and twenty-five, the rate slows still further to 16 or 18 times a minute. Of course, if the body has to work very hard to lift something heavy or to climb a steep hill, or run quickly, it needs more oxygen. Then the rate of breathing suddenly goes up.

A hundred years ago, people used to sleep in rooms with windows tightly shut. They thought

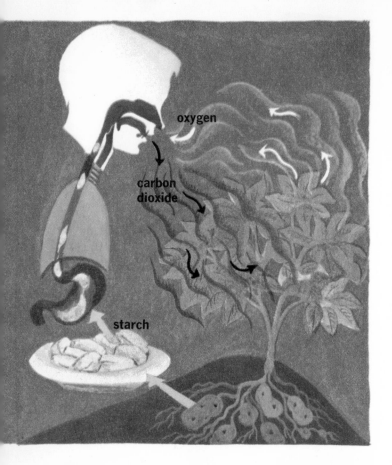

oxygen

carbon
dioxide

starch

Humans inhale oxygen and exhale carbon dioxide. Green plants use carbon dioxide to make oxygen. They store some of the carbon in their roots as starch, which is essential to all animal life.

that the night air carried disease, and the best thing to do was to keep it out. In those days, though, people fell sick to an extent that we would find hard to imagine now. Today, people sleep with windows open enough to let fresh air into the room. Fresh air is needed not only to keep up the supply of oxygen, but to keep air moving around the room. The body feels better in moving air.

Breathing is another example of one of the body's automatic functions. It is different from the activities of the stomach or intestine, however, because we can, if we put our minds to it, breathe at any speed we want. Laughing, coughing, sucking, and blowing are all forms of controlled breathing. Most of the time, though, the body regulates breathing without our even being conscious of the rate of speed.

Breathing is controlled by a group of cells scattered through a section of the brain stem called the respiratory center. These cells are connected to other nerve cells that control the diaphragm and the other muscles that move the ribs. They receive impulses from nerves in the lungs that tell them how much the lungs are inflated. When a certain point has been reached, the respiratory center directs the breathing muscles to relax, and expiration begins.

Nerve impulses from other parts of the body can also influence the rate and speed of breathing. For example, if too much carbon dioxide has collected in the blood, the breathing rate speeds up to dispose of it more rapidly. During exercise, nerves in the muscles telegraph the respiratory center for a more rapid rate, since more oxygen is required. These are just two of the many kinds of influences in the body that affect breathing to allow the body to function most efficiently.

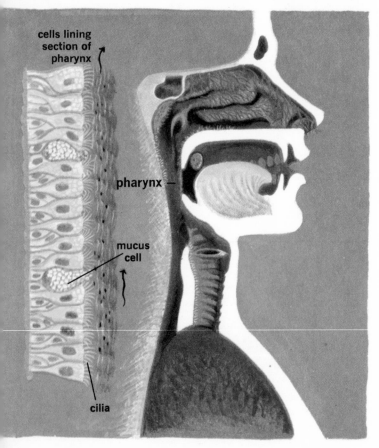

cells lining
section of
pharynx

pharynx

mucus
cell

cilia

In the nasal passages, the pharynx, and the windpipe, there are numerous tiny hairs called cilia. By their constant wavelike motion, they push dust and dirt up and out to clean the air going to the lungs.

Highways for Food and Energy

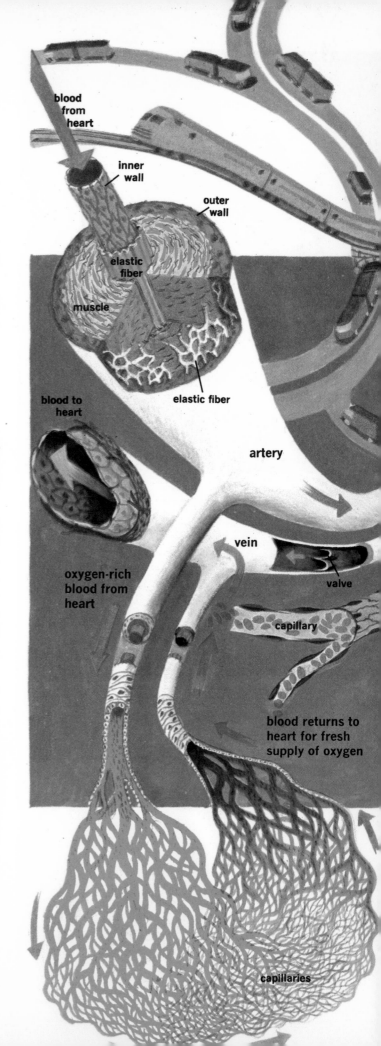

THE TRUCKS and trains that carry the nation's freight do not wander at random over the countryside. Instead, they travel over highways and railway tracks that connect the different parts of the country directly with each other. In the same way, the blood could not supply the body's billions of cells with the nourishment they need if it flowed aimlessly back and forth throughout the body. Like trucks and trains, the blood flows over special highways. These highways are the tubes of muscular tissue that are called blood vessels.

The blood is forced through the body by the pumping action of the heart. After it has been forced out of the heart, the blood moves through the large blood vessels called arteries. Arteries extend throughout the body. Those nearest the heart are fairly large—like the eight-lane highways that lead away from major cities. As they get farther away from the heart, the arteries divide and split into smaller and more numerous arteries, just as highways branch into smaller roads.

As the branches of an artery become smaller and smaller, they narrow down until they are thinner than hairs. They become so thin that the blood moves through them slowly—just as a delivery truck must thread its way slowly along a narrow, twisting country lane far from a main highway.

Because they are so narrow and hairlike, these tiny branches are called capillaries, from the Latin word for hair. In the capillaries, the slowly moving blood delivers food and oxygen to the cells. At the same time, it picks up the waste materials that the cells must get rid of.

Once it has delivered its cargo of oxygen and food and picked up its return load of waste materials, the blood continues to flow along the capillaries, which now begin to come together.

The body's blood vessels resemble a rail or highway system. Food and oxygen move through the arteries, and are delivered to their destination in the body by capillaries. Veins bring back the return load.

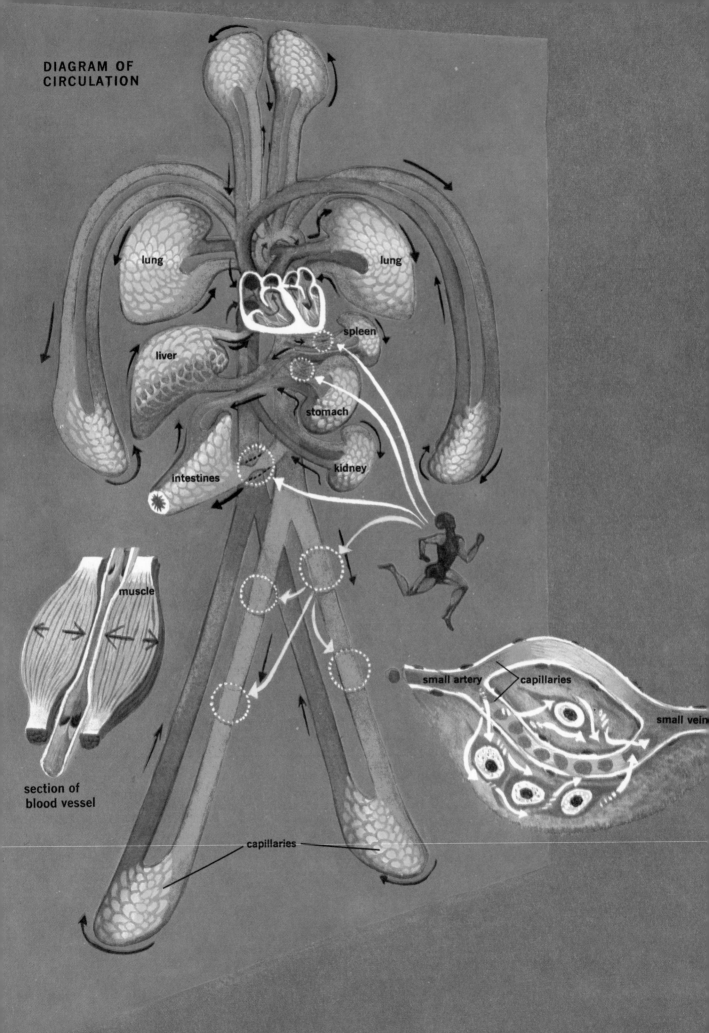

DIAGRAM OF
CIRCULATION

lung

lung

spleen

liver

stomach

intestines

kidney

muscle

small artery

capillaries

small vein

section of
blood vessel

capillaries

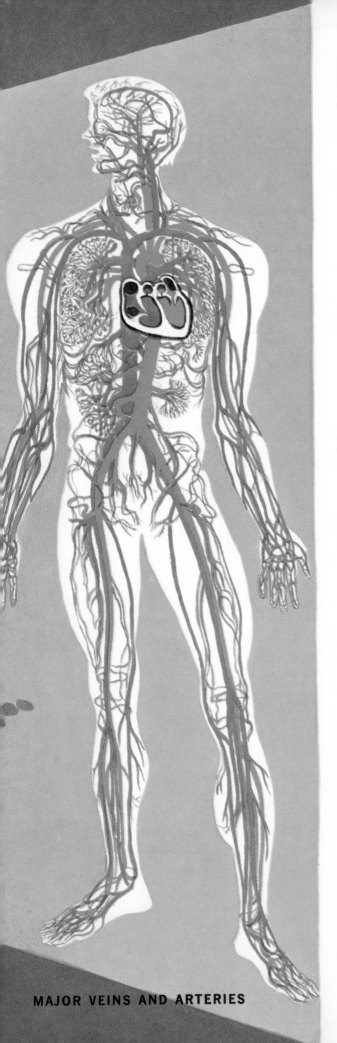

MAJOR VEINS AND ARTERIES

Gradually there are formed larger and larger blood vessels that will return the blood to the heart. The blood vessels that take the blood back to the heart are called veins.

Look at the underside of your wrist. Put your finger on the upper part of the wrist, close to the base of the thumb. If you find the right spot, you will feel a steady beating under the skin. This beating is the pulse, and it is caused by the flow of blood that is being pumped through one of the wrist's arteries. Each beat is caused by a beat of the heart.

The artery by which the pulse is determined can only be felt; it cannot be seen. However, in various parts of the body there are small blue lines under the skin that can be seen. The color of these lines shows that they are veins, not arteries.

Blood in the arteries is bright red. The color comes from the oxygen the arteries carry. Blood in veins is darker because it has lost its oxygen.

When the doctor makes a blood test, he sometimes does so by pricking his patient's finger with a sharp instrument. A small drop of dark red blood appears. The red color is due to a special protein in the blood called hemoglobin. When hemoglobin is carried to the lungs, it picks up oxygen and turns a light red. When it is pumped through the bloodstream into the body's tissues, it gives up its oxygen and becomes a darker, bluish red. Then it enters the veins and returns to the heart and lungs for a new supply of oxygen. Without hemoglobin, there would be no efficient way to transport oxygen to all the tissues of the body.

Blood moves along the major arteries at a fairly fast rate of speed. In some of them, it moves more than a foot a second, much faster than it passes through the capillaries. In the veins, on its return trip to the heart, blood moves at a rate of about four inches a second.

For the most part, arteries and veins travel and branch out through the body side by side, like the opposite sides of a highway.

During exercise, the muscular walls of some of the arteries squeeze to reduce the flow of blood going to the intestinal organs, as shown at left by white arrows. At the same time, other arteries relax to increase the flow of blood to the muscles, as shown by yellow arrows, to give them added nourishment.

Arteries are stronger than veins. Their walls have to be thicker because the blood is pumped through them with far more force and pressure than it is pumped through the veins. Veins are more delicate, but wider.

Blood must not only be kept flowing constantly, but it must be kept flowing in the right direction. Because of this, veins have little valves spaced at intervals along their length to make sure the blood does not flow backward. These valves work in the same way as the valves in bicycle tires that allow air to be pumped in but do not allow it to escape.

When an artery is cut, blood is pumped out through the opening every time the heart beats. One way of stopping the bleeding is by pressing on the artery between the cut and the heart. If the cut is on an arm or a leg, for example, bleeding can be stopped with a special bandage called a tourniquet. The tourniquet is placed around the arm or leg above the cut and is twisted tight to stop all flow of blood. It must be loosened from time to time, however, or the tissues will die from lack of nourishment.

Blood from a cut vein, unlike that from an artery, flows slowly. To stop a vein from bleeding, the bandage must be placed below the cut, on the side away from the heart.

The reason why blood spurts out of a cut artery, but flows only slowly from a vein, is a result of the structure and function of each. When the heart pumps blood into an artery, the artery's thick, elastic walls stretch, then spring back to their original shape. This action pushes the blood forward.

Pressure in the veins is far less than in the arteries. Blood entering the veins comes from the capillaries with most of its pressure gone. What little pressure is left must be passed on gently, for the veins have thin, fragile walls. Since the pressure is light and constant in the veins, blood flows smoothly and evenly.

The amount of blood pressure varies not only between arteries and veins; it may vary in the same artery or vein from one moment to the next. Excitement, emotion, exercise, and substances such as adrenaline make blood pressure rise. Blood pressure is also high during certain illnesses. During an operation, or when the body is suffering from some weakening disease, blood pressure may be quite low.

Because of the relationship between blood pressure and disease, it is often useful for the doctor to measure this pressure. Of course, the pressure in the arteries and that in the veins must be measured separately.

The blood pressure of any one person varies constantly, depending upon whether that person is active or still, excited or calm. There is a wide range of blood pressures that may be called normal, but in general, pressure is lower in children than in adults, and higher in older adults than in younger ones. These variations are perfectly normal, and—within certain limits—do not indicate that there is anything wrong with the person.

Blood pressure is measured in millimeters of mercury. By one technique, doctors take an armlet, or flat rubber bag covered with cloth, and wrap it around the patient's arm, just above the elbow. In the armlet are two rubber tubes. One leads to a manometer—an instrument that contains a tube of mercury and a scale showing millimeters. The other tube is attached to a rubber bulb, and a valve. The rubber bulb is used to pump air into the armlet. When the air pressure of the armlet is equal to the blood pressure of the artery of the arm, the pulse stops.

The doctor slowly releases the air in the armlet. At the same time, he listens through a stethoscope that is placed just below the armlet. As blood starts flowing again through the arm, there is a strong beat. As the armlet continues to deflate the beat disappears and is replaced by a faint beat. The reading of the millimeter scale for each of these beats gives the blood pressure.

Veins, arteries, capillaries, and lymph vessels make up the circulatory system.

How the blood circulates through the body was for centuries a puzzle to man. In ancient times, it was thought that blood moved only through the veins, and that the arteries transported air. The true explanation was not put forward until the time the English settled America. William Harvey—doctor, anatomist, and physiologist—was the first to describe the circulation of the blood.

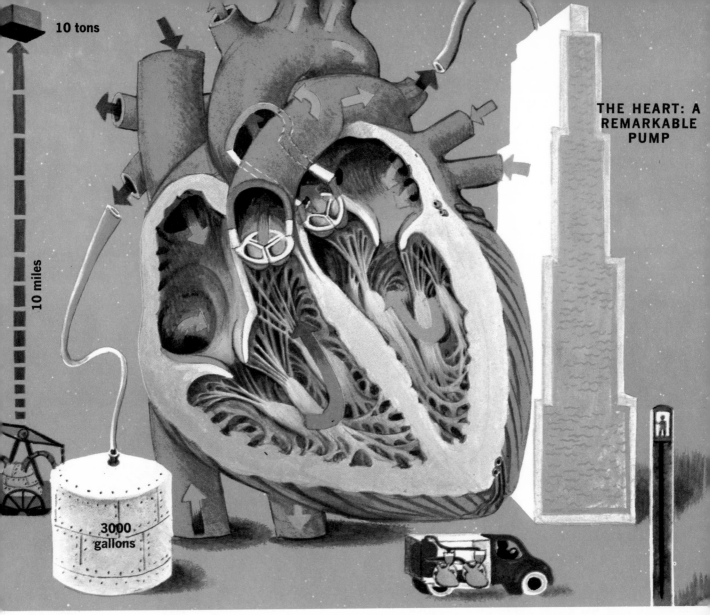

3000 gallons

The heart is a powerful instrument, pumping about three thousand gallons of blood daily. In a lifetime of seventy years, a heart could pump roughly 77,000,000 gallons of blood—enough to fill a skyscraper—or raise a ten ton weight ten miles. In an hour, a heart could raise a man five floors in an elevator. Two hearts could provide enough power to drive a truck around the world in two years.

The Heart of the Matter

Until 1628, when William Harvey published his short book describing the circulation of the blood and the workings of the heart, no one really knew what the heart did or how it worked. It was thought that it had something to do with the blood, but people generally considered it to be the place in the body where love and courage are felt. Until Harvey's discovery, no one realized that the heart is one of the toughest muscles in the human body, and one of the most amazing pumps in the world. It is the heart that pumps the blood night and day throughout the body. Though it is no bigger than a clenched fist, it does enough work during a single day to lift a man weighing 150 pounds almost 1000 feet into the air.

The heart is really two pumps, side by side—one on the right and one on the left. The pump on the right sends blood from the veins to the

101

lungs. Then it pumps blood through the lungs to the pump on the left, which sends it through the body.

This is how it works. Each pump consists of two hollow chambers, one above the other. The upper, thin-walled chamber is called the auricle. The lower chamber, thick-walled and more powerful, is called the ventricle. The two chambers are separated by valves that allow the blood to flow in only one direction. When blood enters the heart, it flows through the veins into the right auricle. The blood pours into the auricle and down through open valves into the ventricle. The auricle helps this flow slightly by a brief squeezing action just before the ventricle begins its contraction.

As the ventricle contracts, the valves between the auricle and the ventricle shut to keep the blood from returning to the auricle. The blood can then go only one way—out of the ventricle through other valves that open into the large artery leading to the lung.

The blood is forced through the lung where it picks up oxygen and deposits carbon dioxide. It cannot return to the heart because valves at the exits of the ventricles snap shut at the end of the heartbeat. When the blood has completed its work in the lungs, it is collected into large veins and flows to the left side of the heart.

On the left side of the heart, the pump has two chambers, exactly as on the right. The blood is

The Heart Cycle. 1. Blood from veins enters upper heart chambers (auricles). 2. The auricles contract and force blood into lower chambers (ventricles). 3. Ventricles contract, close valves from auricles, and open valves to arteries. Blood from the right ventricle is pumped through arteries to the lungs; blood from the left ventricle goes into the artery that supplies the body. 4. The cycle starts over.

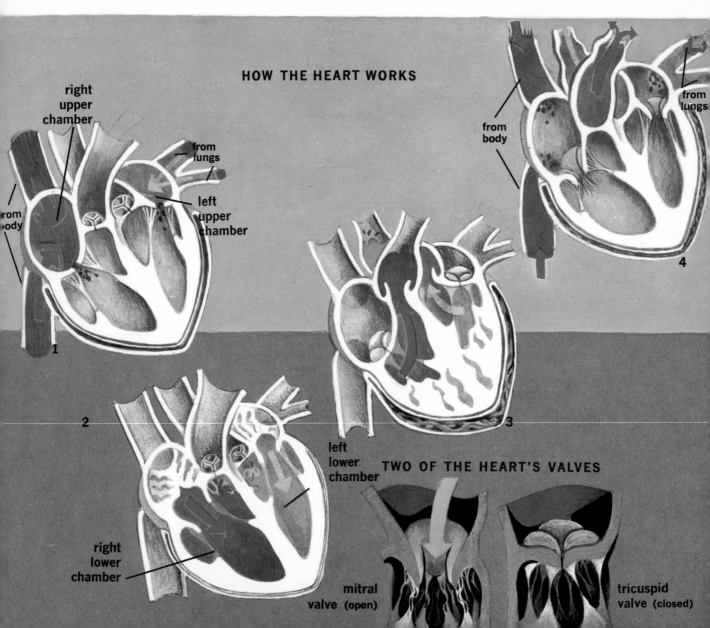

HOW THE HEART WORKS

right upper chamber

from lungs

left upper chamber

from body

from lungs

from body

from lungs

1

4

2

3

left lower chamber

TWO OF THE HEART'S VALVES

right lower chamber

mitral valve (open)

tricuspid valve (closed)

pumped from the upper left chamber to the lower left chamber. The lower left chamber sends the blood to the main artery of the body, which is called the aorta. From the aorta, the blood passes on to the different branches of the arteries and is pumped throughout the body.

Because the left side of the heart has to pump blood a far greater distance than the right side, the muscle walls of the left lower chamber are more than twice as thick and strong as the walls of the right side.

Each time the muscles of the heart contract, two ounces of blood are sent out from the right and left ventricles. The heart beats about 72 times a minute. In half an hour, it is able to pump about 260 quarts of blood. Since there are only about six to seven quarts of blood in a full-grown man, the blood has to circulate through the body at a fairly fast rate. However, in certain diseases, the rate of speed at which the blood circulates may be faster or slower than normal.

The rate of the heartbeat is regulated by two sets of nerves. One makes the heart beat faster; the other slows it down. The nerve that makes the heart beat faster is called the accelerator nerve. The nerve that slows it down is called the vagus nerve. But we cannot change the rate of our heartbeat by deciding to do so. This is because the accelerator and vagus nerves are controlled by a part of the nervous system that works automatically. The heart, however, can beat independently of the nerves. The nerves simply change the speed of the heartbeat to conform to the body's requirements.

When the heart stroke is weak, the beat is fast in order to keep up the correct flow. A steady beat is full of strength. The heartbeat has three parts. The first part is the squeeze, the second part is the relaxation, and the third part is a period of rest. The period of rest is much shorter than the other two parts put together. When your heart beats fast, it is only the rest period that is shortened, not the time for the strokes.

If you listen to someone's heart, you will hear sounds like *lubb dup . . . lubb dup . . . lubb dup*. The sounds are the closing of the heart valves, first in one chamber, then in the other. The sounds last a little longer than the time needed for the valve to close, because each sound causes echoes inside the chest.

The rate of heartbeat is not the same for all animals. An elephant's heart beats only 25 times a minute; a mouse's about 700. If you have ever held a bird in your hand, you can feel a very rapid heartbeat. Most people think this is because the bird is frightened, but the rate of a bird's heartbeat is normally much higher than a human being's. Even in a human being, the rate changes. A newborn baby's heart beats 140 times a minute. A three-year-old child's heartbeat is about 100. The heartbeat continues to slow down for a full-grown person to an average rate, subject to considerable variation, of about 72 beats per minute.

During exercise, the rate of the heartbeat speeds up rapidly. This is largely brought about by a reflex action on the part of the nerves that affect the heartbeat. Fear and excitement also cause the rate of the heartbeat to speed up.

After a session of heavy exercise, the heart beats faster than normal for several reasons. For one thing, muscles that have been working need more food and oxygen than muscles that are quiet or at rest. For another, the blood is warmer after exercise than before it. If the body is not to become overheated, the warm blood must circulate faster, and the heart pump harder.

Even though the right- and left-hand sides of the heart are two different pumps with no direct connection between them, they squeeze and relax in just about the same rhythm. Together they pump about 13,000 quarts of blood through the body every day.

The most wonderful thing about the heart is that it goes on beating throughout life, resting only a fraction of a second after each beat. Since this involves over 100,000 beats per day, the durability of this organ is obviously great.

Doctors once thought that the heart was an organ that could not be operated on. In recent years, however, surgeons have been able to operate on more and more people with afflicted hearts. They have often been able to make them strong and healthy by various types of operations. The surgeons have been helped in this by wonderful machines that act as substitute hearts and lungs while the patient is being worked on.

The Work of the Cells

RAILROAD trains, trucks, and airplanes travel back and forth across the country delivering freight so that every house on every street in every town is supplied with what it needs. The body has an even more wonderful delivery system. It takes oxygen from the lungs and food from the small intestine to every one of its several billion cells. Blood and lymph are the body's delivery agents.

When someone cuts his finger, the blood that flows from the cut looks red. However, blood looks red only because the eye cannot see very small things as easily as it can see large things. Actually, blood is not a red fluid at all.

An eye that could see the tiny things of the world would find that blood is a clear, pale yellow liquid, almost like water. Floating around in it are great numbers of flat, round, red cells. A closer look would find other cells that are harder to see at first because they are the same watery color as the liquid in which they float. Some of these white cells have no regular shape. They move themselves about by changing their shape.

In the human body there are more than 500 times as many red cells as there are white ones; and the number of red cells in a healthy person is about twenty trillion.

The blood circulates through the entire body. Each of the three main parts of the blood—the red cells, the white cells, and the clear yellow fluid—has its special job. Together they feed, supply, and even defend the cells of tissue that make up the human body.

Blood cells are developed in the marrow of certain bones such as the ribs. Below is a highly magnified view of rib marrow, with different kinds of blood cells developing and entering the bloodstream.

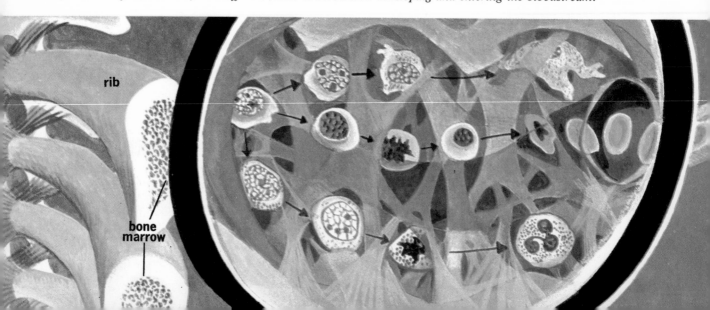

rib

bone marrow

The clear yellowish liquid, which is the fluid part of the blood, is called serum. It carries food to the cells of the tissues and removes waste materials. It also contains special substances called antibodies that protect the body from infection.

When the blood reaches the capillaries, part of the serum leaks out through the capillary walls. Some of it re-enters the capillary further along, but the rest flows outside the vessels among the cells. It is finally collected into tiny lymph vessels which are widely distributed throughout the body. These join to form larger vessels and eventually connect with the veins. In this way, the lymph is returned to the bloodstream.

In its course through the lymph vessels, the fluid passes through lymph nodes that filter out any harmful substances—such as bacteria—that may have been collected. There are so many lymph vessels in the skin that any kind of cut will tear into them. Foreign substances, therefore, get into the lymph vessels fairly easily. Once there, they are trapped and kept from spreading through the system.

The lymph and veins first receive food material from the hairlike villi of the small intestine. Fats are absorbed into the lymph vessels; amino acids and glucose into the veins. In general, the job of taking food materials to the various parts of the body is done by the blood. Lymph then takes over to deliver these materials to the cells. In this way, the delivery system of blood and lymph carries the liquid food to the billions of tissue cells. Afterward, lymph fluid returns to the veins to complete the circulation to the heart.

The blood is also given the job of delivering oxygen to the tissue cells. Railroad trains have special cars to carry gasoline. The blood, in the same way, has its special carriers to deliver oxygen. These are the red cells.

Red cells are so small that 75 billion of them would fit into a one-inch cube. They are round discs thinned out in the center in such a way that they resemble two saucers placed together with a raised rubber border between them. They are elastic so they can be squeezed out of shape to pass something in their way, but they quickly snap back to their regular form. Singly they are not red, but yellowish.

Red cells get their color from hemoglobin, a protein that contains iron. The cells pick up oxygen from the air sacs in the lungs and carry it to the tissues in their hemoglobin. There the oxygen is released, goes into the plasma of the blood, and is carried directly to the tissues. Carbon dioxide is simultaneously picked up by the blood.

When the blood has picked up carbon dioxide, it returns to the lungs where it gives up this waste gas to the air in the air sacs. The gas is then exhaled. In the lungs, the red cells, which have lost their oxygen to the tissues, pick up a new load to distribute throughout the body.

The white cells that circulate in the bloodstream have nothing to do with the delivery of food and oxygen. They are roaming bodies of policemen whose job it is to protect the body against foreign substances such as bacteria.

Certain white cells, because they have no regular shape, can smother enemy particles by flowing

The wandering white cells are able to pass into and out of the thin-walled blood vessels. They are the policemen of the body, destroying any foreign particles they come across.

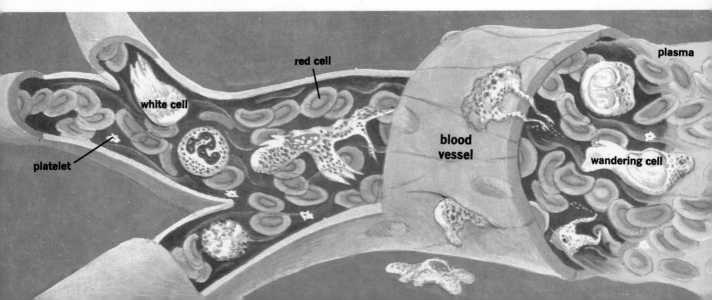

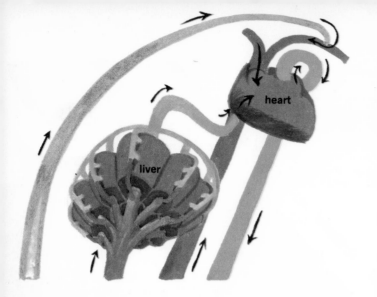

Food that is prepared for the body's cells in the small intestine is collected by the veins and the lymph vessels. The transporting of food particles over long distances is done by the blood.

around them. When the enemy particle is inside the white cell, it is dissolved in special fluids which the white cell gives off. There are other kinds of white cells, too. Each does its own job of protection, although the exact function of many of them is still not known.

When the body is infected by swarms of enemy bacteria, the number of white cells in the blood is increased, as if extra troops were being called out.

Red blood cells are manufactured in the marrow of the bones. A young red cell has a nucleus, like any other cell; but after a while this nucleus disappears. The red cell then leaves the marrow and passes into the bloodstream; there it is no longer a true cell, but simply an envelope to carry oxygen to the cells.

White cells, on the other hand, are true cells with their own nuclei, whether they are in the bone marrow or lymph tissue where they are born, or circulating in the bloodstream.

In the tiny, thin-walled blood vessels called capillaries, oxygen is released by the red cells and given up to the cells of the tissues. Carbon dioxide is then picked up and carried through the veins to the lungs, where it is exhaled.

heart

liver

aorta

lymph vessel

vein to liver

vein to heart

food

fat

small intestine

red cells release oxygen

carbon dioxide is taken to lungs

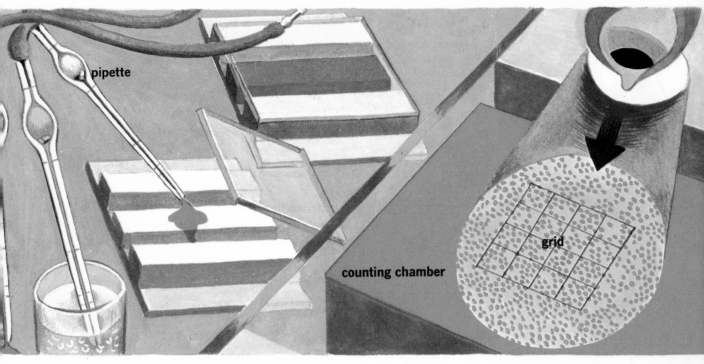

pipette

grid

counting chamber

When a blood count is taken, a small amount of blood is drawn into a pipette, diluted with a special fluid, and released on a counting chamber. The counting chamber has a grid on it. When looked at through a microscope, the number of blood cells on the grid can easily be counted.

More about the Blood

Men may have learned fairly early in history about bandaging, and how necessary it is to stop the flow of blood from a cut or a wound. However, the human race wouldn't have lasted long enough to learn even this if nature hadn't given the body its own way of stopping bleeding.

If blood did not have the power to clot, the slightest cut would mean continual bleeding until the body was emptied. Although bandages are often helpful and sometimes necessary, there are many times when they are not needed. In a short time, most cuts and abrasions form a dark red scab, or clot, that stops the bleeding.

The next time you scrape your flesh enough for it to bleed a little, watch for a while to see what happens. The flow stops as the blood forms a soft cap over the wound. As this cap dries and hardens, you may notice a yellowish or white fluid around the edges. This is the serum being squeezed out as the clot hardens.

Clotting is a complicated process involving four substances: calcium, and three proteins called fibrinogen, prothrombin, and thromboplastin.

Clotting is begun when a blood vessel is injured. Blood comes into contact with the tissue around the injury, and the prothrombin in the tissue unites with the calcium and thromboplastin in the bloodstream. The prothrombin is changed into another substance, called thrombin, which unites with the fibrinogen to form a network of a threadlike substance called fibrin that traps red and white cells in its meshes.

The red cells give the color to a clot, although white cells are trapped, too. The clot, in addition to acting like a plug in a leaking dike, forms the foundation on which the new tissue will be built to heal the wound.

The way the blood clots is so complicated and involves so many factors that it can easily go wrong if one or another of the various ingredients

107

DIAGRAM OF BLOOD TYPES

blood cells of donor	serum of receiver			
	A	**B**	**AB**	**O**
A	solid (mix)	dotted (not)	solid (mix)	dotted (not)
B	dotted (not)	solid (mix)	solid (mix)	dotted (not)
AB	dotted (not)	dotted (not)	solid (mix)	dotted (not)
O	solid (mix)	solid (mix)	solid (mix)	solid (mix)

(labels in the top-left testing illustration: blood, serum, matching, non-matching)

Before a transfusion, the blood types of both donor and receiver must be tested to see if they are the same. The diagram above shows the four main types of blood and which ones will mix with which others. The solid red clump means that the two will mix, the dotted red means they will not.

is missing. There are a number of blood disorders that cause people to bleed excessively or fail to produce clots properly. The amazing thing is not that these defects occur, but that they are so rare.

Blood clotting occurs for the most part only when the blood is exposed to air. That is why the blood does not clot inside the body. If it did (and it does occasionally in certain diseases), then the flow of blood would be stopped, and this would be dangerous.

Too much flow of blood from a wound can also be dangerous. For hundreds of years, men looked for a way to replace lost blood with blood from a healthy person. Everyone who tried failed until scientists found that there were really four different types of blood. Today, in the process called transfusion, blood can be given from one person to another if both have the same or compatible types of blood.

If two different types of blood are mixed, the red cells clump together with dangerous results. To test whether two bloods are of the same type,

How a wound heals. 1. A splinter enters the skin, bringing with it harmful bacteria. White blood cells surround and destroy the bacteria. 2. White blood cells continue to keep the wound clean; the blood clots; fluid enters the wound. 3. Connective tissue cells come into the wound and intertwine.

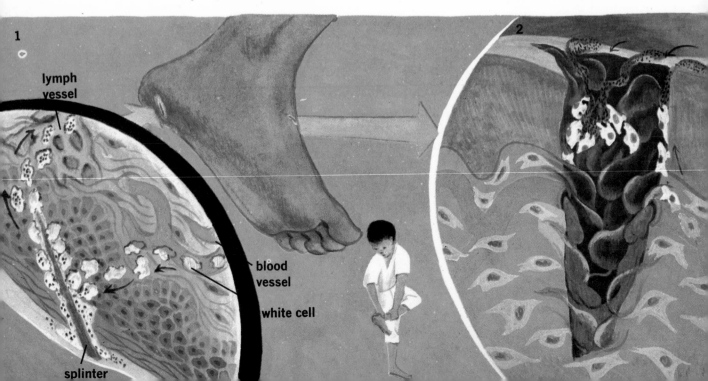

1

lymph vessel

blood vessel

white cell

splinter

2

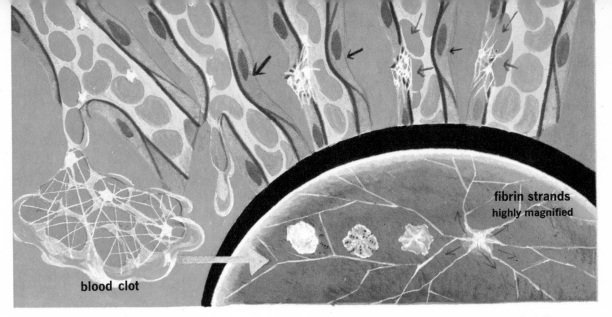

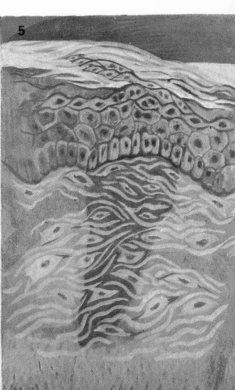

For blood to clot, two substances—one in the blood, the other in tissue—and a protein called fibrinogen are necessary. When a blood vessel breaks, the two substances combine. They change the fibrinogen into threadlike fibrin which acts like a net and gathers in and traps the blood cells.

the serum of one blood is added to some cells from the other. If the red cells don't form clumps, then the two bloods are either of the same type or are compatible.

One type of blood does not form clumps with any other type. In an emergency, it can be used for transfusions for any type of blood. However, it is preferable to use identical types for transfusions. In every case, the blood cells from the person giving the blood must be mixed with the serum of the person receiving it, regardless of

blood type. This must be done before the transfusion to make sure that the two will mix and that there will be no clumping.

So much is now known about blood transfusion that hospitals collect blood from people who are healthy enough to be able to spare a pint or two. Sometimes, during an operation, there is a serious loss of blood from the patient. A pint or two of preserved blood restores the patient's strength at once. Thousands of soldiers' lives have been saved by transfusions in time of war.

As the wound continues to heal, blood vessels put forth new cells to form new blood vessels. 4. New scar tissue forms through the area of the wound. 5. Cells of skin grow and spread over the scar tissue. The blood vessels have knit together and the wound is healed.

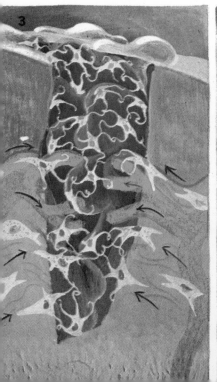

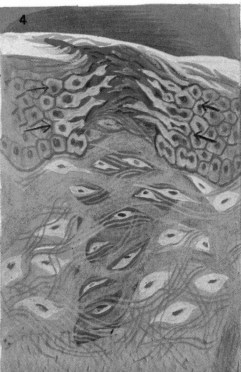

The Lymph

Very early in this book, in the chapter dealing with cells, it was stated that the single cells of the body are mostly fluid and for that reason live in fluid. This fluid is called lymph.

The lymph is very similar to ocean water. It is salty, and contains the same salts that are found in the sea, except in smaller amounts. This is probably not an accident. Life itself may have begun in the sea many millions of years ago, when the sea was less salty than it is now; the amounts of salts in the lymph may be what they were in the primeval sea.

The lymph fluid is a part of the whole blood that has flowed out of the blood vessels, leaving the red blood cells behind. The lymph therefore has a watery color. It bathes the individual cells, feeding them with the nourishing substances that came from the small intestine.

Lymph flows from the spaces within the tissues into the lymph vessels and passes through progressively larger vessels into the veins. On the way, it filters through little balls of cells called lymph nodes.

These nodes act as cleansing stations where the bacteria and waste products from the cells are removed. For example, tonsils are lymph nodes; but since there are plenty of other lymph nodes in the body, infected tonsils can be removed without slowing down the purifying job. The other lymph nodes simply take over.

When bacteria enter the body and cause infection, some of the bacteria pass into the lymph vessels. They are carried along these vessels to a lymph node where they are destroyed.

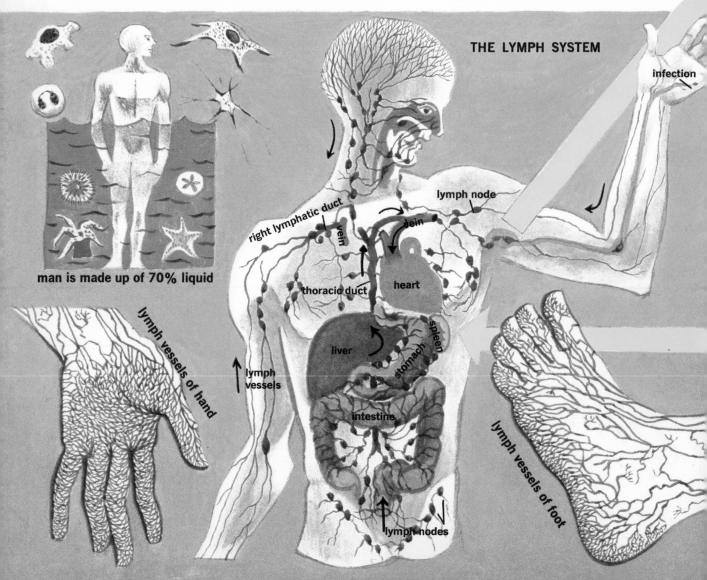

man is made up of 70% liquid

THE LYMPH SYSTEM

infection

right lymphatic duct

vein

vein

lymph node

thoracic duct

heart

lymph vessels of hand

lymph vessels

liver

spleen

stomach

intestine

lymph nodes

lymph vessels of foot

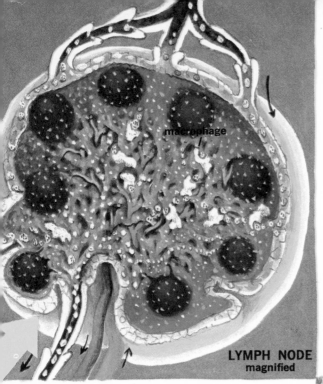

LYMPH NODE
magnified

little smaller than a clenched fist, lies next to the stomach in the upper left side of the abdomen. It is made up of clusters of white blood cells like those found in lymph nodes, and of spaces through which blood flows.

The chief functions of the spleen are to manufacture white blood cells, destroy worn-out red blood cells, and act as a blood storage reservoir. Despite these important activities, the spleen can be removed without much harm to the person.

The number of lymph vessels in the body is far greater than the number of blood vessels. They start at the skin as tiny threadlike capillaries; then they pass deeper into the body toward the heart. The branches join to form larger vessels called lymph trunks.

Many white cells originate in the lymph nodes. While these cells probably help in the body's defense against infection, their exact function is not clearly known. It may be that some of the substances made by the body to help it combat infection are manufactured within these cells. However, the cells do not move to the place where the infection is and engulf bacteria, as many other white cells do.

One of the most interesting parts of the lymph system is the spleen. This organ, a

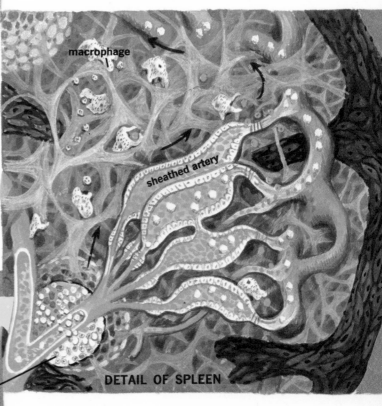

DETAIL OF SPLEEN

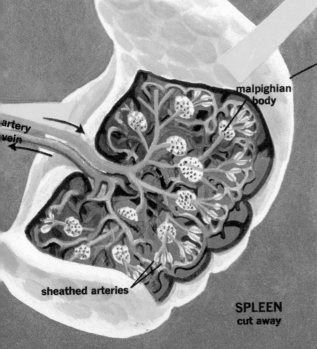

SPLEEN
cut away

Large white cells called macrophages in the lymph nodes destroy invading or foreign cells. The lymph nodes also produce a fluid substance that aids the body in combating infection. The spleen has similar functions, but it also destroys old or worn-out red blood cells and acts as a reservoir for blood to be used in emergencies. It contains special structures called malpighian bodies that produce certain white blood cells.

111

The Liver

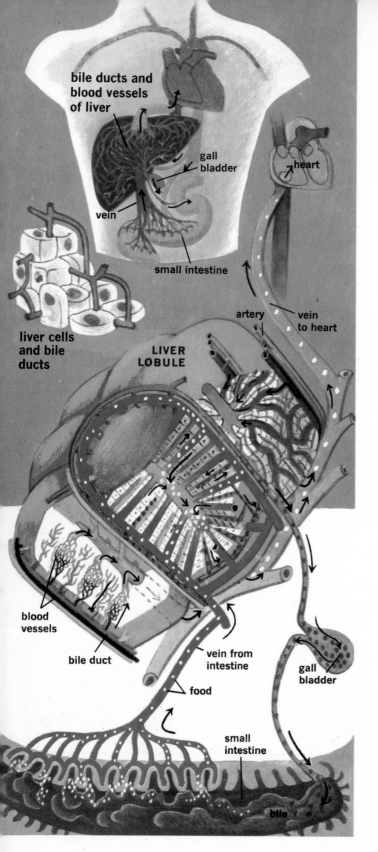

bile ducts and blood vessels of liver

gall bladder

heart

vein

small intestine

liver cells and bile ducts

artery

vein to heart

LIVER LOBULE

blood vessels

bile duct

vein from intestine

gall bladder

food

small intestine

bile

The above diagram of a liver lobule gives an idea of the complexity of the liver's structure. There are innumerable such lobules in the liver. The diagram also shows how bile is sent into the small intestine, and how food particles are absorbed through veins into the liver before being delivered to the body cells.

IN ANCIENT DAYS, people believed that certain parts of the body had magical properties. For instance, the Romans believed they could tell what was going to happen from the shape and size of the liver of an animal that had been sacrificed. Men believed that the liver was the very center of life, that it was where one thought and felt and where the blood came from.

Today we know that the brain is the center of thought. We know that the heart is the pump for blood. We also know so much about the liver that we can say it is even more important than the ancients thought. We may not think it is magic; we do know that it is marvelous.

By placing your hand on the lower ribs at the right side of your chest, you will be placing it over the liver. The liver weighs about four times as much as the heart. It is about eight or nine inches wide, four to five inches thick, and six to seven inches high. It is divided into two main parts called "lobes." Two sets of blood vessels enter it.

Think of the liver as a great mass of tissue divided into many-sided columns of cells, each one of which is about as big across as a pinhead. Running among these columns are tiny branches of the portal vein carrying food from the intestines, and branches of the hepatic artery bringing oxygen to fuel the liver cells.

In addition to the blood vessels, there are many tiny bile ducts in the liver. They collect the bile secreted by the liver cells and carry it to the gall bladder, where it is stored to be used when needed.

The liver is responsible for the final stage in treatment of proteins, carbohydrates, and fats. Much of this work has been done in the intestine. The intestine breaks carbohydrate down to the simple sugar called glucose.

In the liver, glucose is turned into a form of starch that can be stored. This starch is called glycogen and is also found in muscle. When the body needs glucose, the glycogen stored in the warehouse of the liver is turned back to glucose and released into the blood.

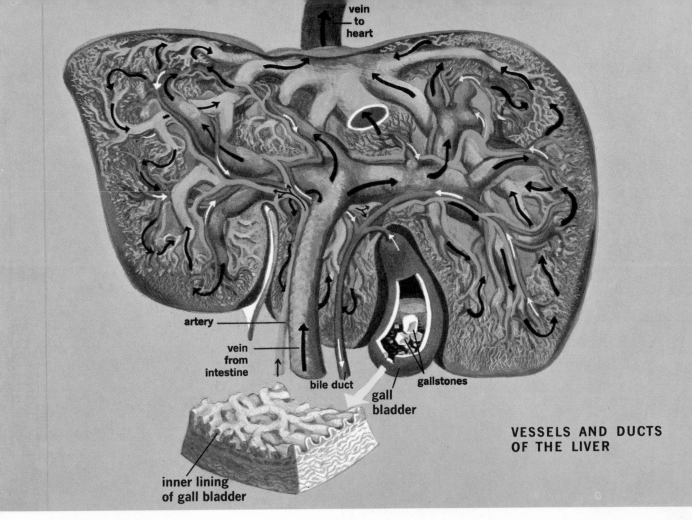

vein
to
heart

artery

vein
from
intestine

bile duct

gall
bladder

gallstones

inner lining
of gall bladder

**VESSELS AND DUCTS
OF THE LIVER**

Bile is a digestive fluid formed in the liver lobules and collected by bile ducts (shown in green, above). The gall bladder stores bile and releases it as necessary. Bile salts sometimes form stones called gallstones. They may block the bile ducts, causing the condition known as jaundice.

Protein in the liver is broken down into the amino acids that the body needs. Those amino acids that are not needed are changed into other substances by the removal of nitrogen. The nitrogen is then sent to the kidneys, from where it is excreted.

Fat is also stored temporarily in the liver. It undergoes changes there and is converted to simpler substances.

The liver is not only the great storehouse and processor of food: it is also a factory for manufacturing the proteins fibrinogen and prothrombin, which help the blood to clot in open wounds. At the same time, the liver manufactures heparin, which keeps the blood from clotting while it circulates through the body. The liver also stores iron for hemoglobin.

The liver manufactures an important fluid called bile, which is generally of a greenish-yellow color.

About two small glassfuls of bile are produced every day. It is stored in the gall bladder. During digestion, bile is poured into the small intestine. There it mixes with food—particularly fat—and helps prepare it to be absorbed into the bloodstream for further action by the liver.

When too much bile is produced, or when the cells are not working properly, bile accumulates in the bloodstream and goes to all parts of the body. This causes the skin to turn a yellowish color. The same thing can happen if the tube that carries bile to the intestine becomes plugged up with stones from the gall bladder. This condition is called jaundice.

In addition to its other functions, the liver is the great protector of the body. When we accidently swallow or inhale poisonous substances, it is often the liver that treats them and renders them harmless.

113

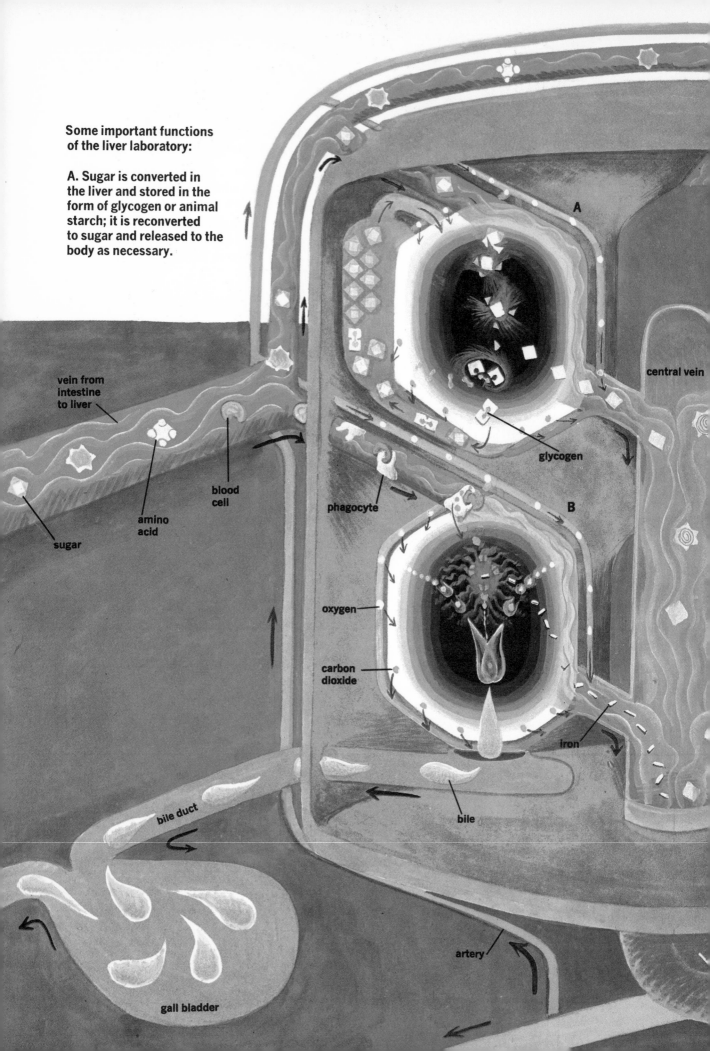

Some important functions
of the liver laboratory:

A. Sugar is converted in
the liver and stored in the
form of glycogen or animal
starch; it is reconverted
to sugar and released to the
body as necessary.

A

central vein

vein from
intestine
to liver

glycogen

blood
cell

amino
acid

phagocyte

B

sugar

oxygen

carbon
dioxide

iron

bile duct

bile

artery

gall bladder

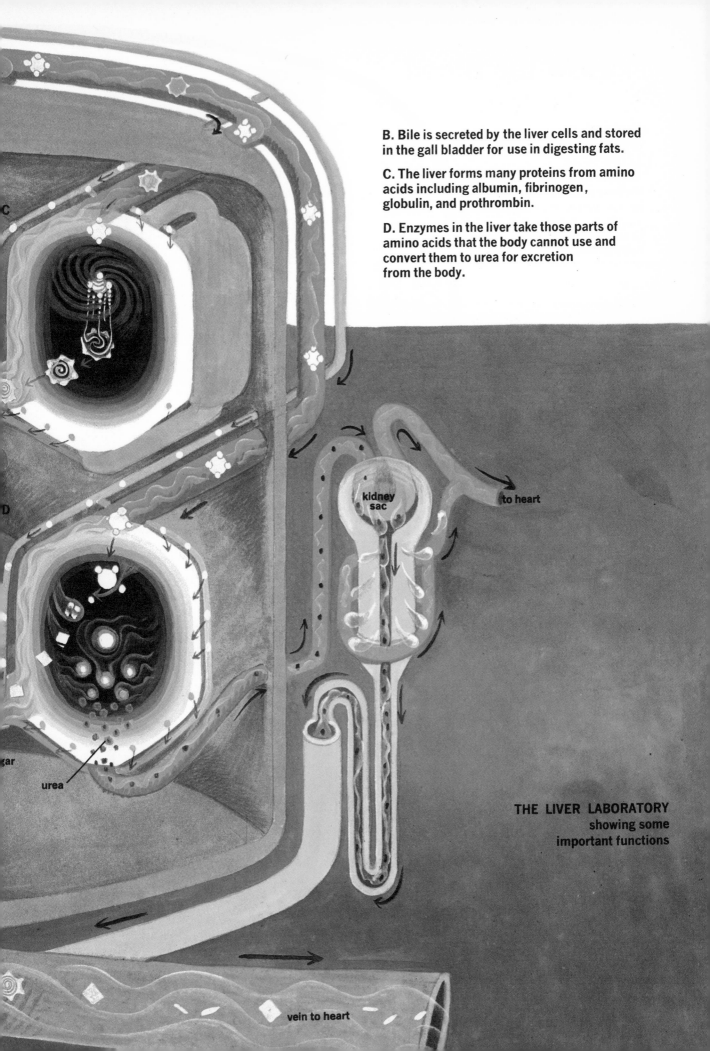

B. Bile is secreted by the liver cells and stored in the gall bladder for use in digesting fats.

C. The liver forms many proteins from amino acids including albumin, fibrinogen, globulin, and prothrombin.

D. Enzymes in the liver take those parts of amino acids that the body cannot use and convert them to urea for excretion from the body.

C

D

kidney sac

to heart

gar

urea

THE LIVER LABORATORY
showing some
important functions

vein to heart

How the Blood Is Purified

W<small>HEN</small> energy for living is produced in the body's myriad cells, the food substances are burned down to waste. These wastes must be removed as rapidly as possible.

The blood that brings food and oxygen to the cells of the body also carries away the wastes. To keep the amount of wastes in the body as low as possible, they must be removed as fast as they are formed. The cleansing of the blood is so important to life that the body has a special set of organs for this high-speed purification.

Suppose you had a bucket of sandy water from which you wanted to remove the sand. If you passed the water through a cloth, the water would go through and the sand remain behind. This is filtering. If you were in a hurry, you could pour the water into a cloth bag and squeeze it. The harder you squeeze, the faster the filtered water spurts out. This is filtering under pressure.

The body's high-speed cleansing organs are the kidneys. Each one has more than a million tiny filters. Blood is pumped forcefully to the kidneys from the heart, and in this way the bloodstream is cleansed under pressure.

The body's blood purification system is centered in the kidneys, which filter the blood under pressure.

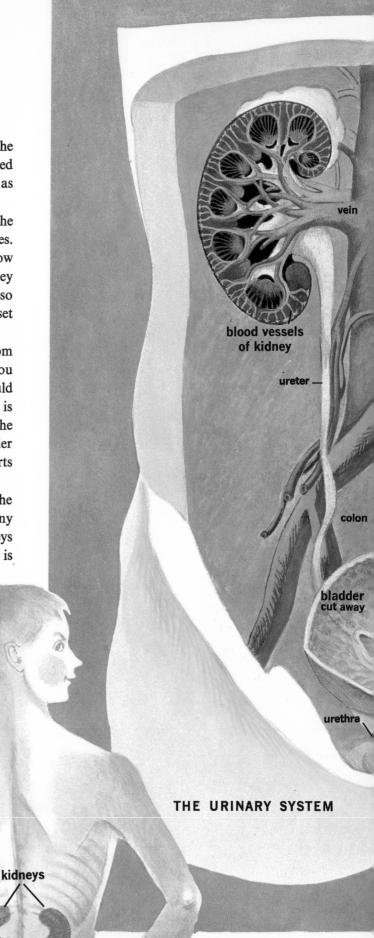

vein

blood vessels of kidney

ureter —

colon

bladder cut away

urethra

kidneys

THE URINARY SYSTEM

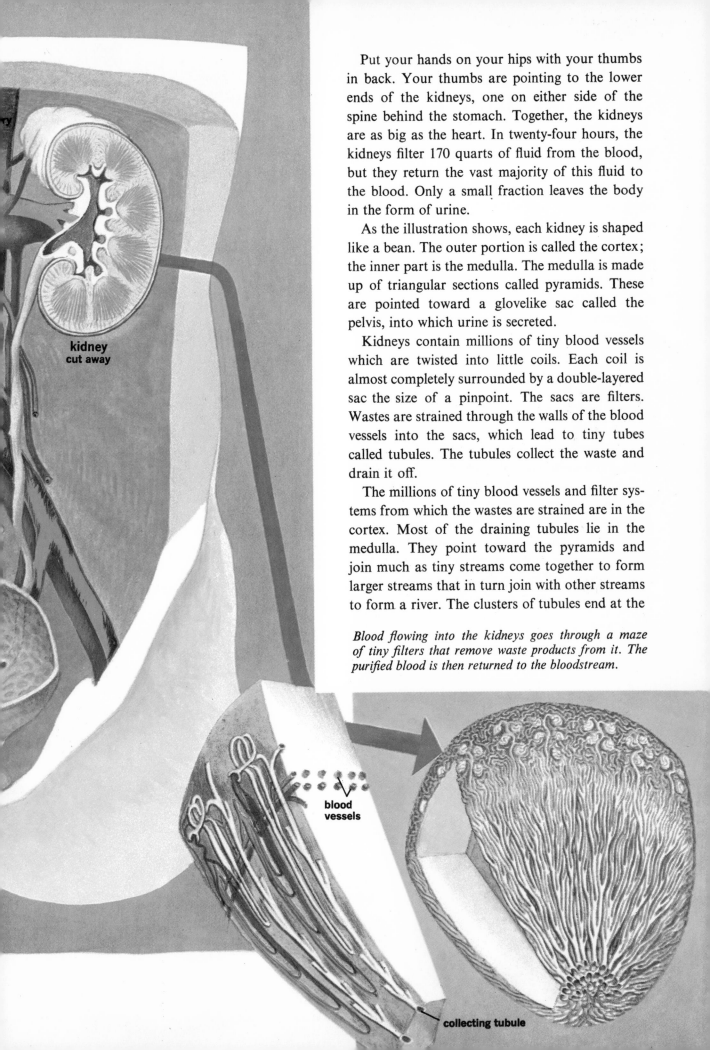

**kidney
cut away**

Put your hands on your hips with your thumbs in back. Your thumbs are pointing to the lower ends of the kidneys, one on either side of the spine behind the stomach. Together, the kidneys are as big as the heart. In twenty-four hours, the kidneys filter 170 quarts of fluid from the blood, but they return the vast majority of this fluid to the blood. Only a small fraction leaves the body in the form of urine.

As the illustration shows, each kidney is shaped like a bean. The outer portion is called the cortex; the inner part is the medulla. The medulla is made up of triangular sections called pyramids. These are pointed toward a glovelike sac called the pelvis, into which urine is secreted.

Kidneys contain millions of tiny blood vessels which are twisted into little coils. Each coil is almost completely surrounded by a double-layered sac the size of a pinpoint. The sacs are filters. Wastes are strained through the walls of the blood vessels into the sacs, which lead to tiny tubes called tubules. The tubules collect the waste and drain it off.

The millions of tiny blood vessels and filter systems from which the wastes are strained are in the cortex. Most of the draining tubules lie in the medulla. They point toward the pyramids and join much as tiny streams come together to form larger streams that in turn join with other streams to form a river. The clusters of tubules end at the

Blood flowing into the kidneys goes through a maze of tiny filters that remove waste products from it. The purified blood is then returned to the bloodstream.

**blood
vessels**

collecting tubule

DIAGRAM OF KIDNEY SAC AND TUBULES

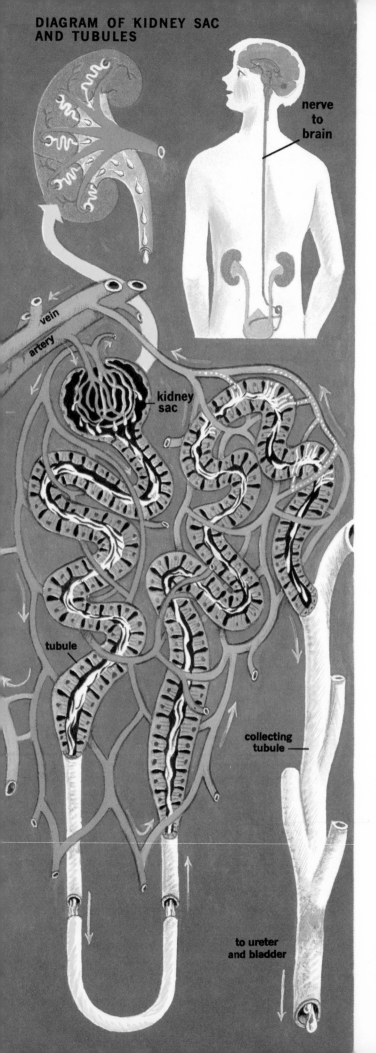

nerve to brain

vein

artery

kidney sac

tubule

collecting tubule

to ureter and bladder

point of each pyramid. There the waste liquids pour into the kidney pelvis.

The liquid wastes that are collected in each kidney are then piped away through a long, hollow tube, the ureter. There is one ureter for each kidney. The ureters are about the size of a macaroni strand. Through the ureters the wastes reach a reservoir called the bladder. The bladder is like a bag. When it is empty, it is flat. When it is full, it is round and projects upward. At the lower end of the bladder is the urethra, through which urine passes out of the body.

Urine enters the bladder a little at a time, and the bag, which has a wall of muscle tissue, slowly fills up. When about a cupful is collected, nerves send messages to the brain. The brain knows that soon the urine will have to be sent out of the body. At the proper time and place, the brain signals to the muscles that control the urethra. A muscular ring around this tube relaxes. The bladder muscle presses down and the accumulated waste liquid is forced out.

When the urinary passage is clogged in one way or another, so that the waste liquids cannot escape freely, a pressure is built up. If this pressure gets too high, the passage of wastes from the blood into the tubules is held up. This causes an accumulation of waste in the bloodstream, and may be a symptom of any of several disorders.

Wastes drain through kidney tubules to the bladder. A nerve signals the brain when the bladder is full.

DROP OF URINE
highly magnified

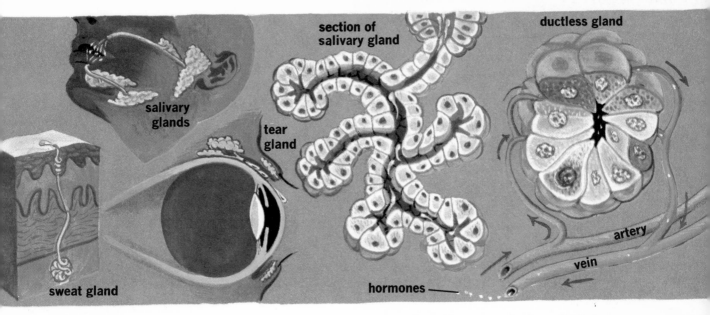

Some glands pour their fluids into the body through tiny openings. The endocrine, or ductless, glands have no such openings. They supply their hormones directly into the bloodstream.

Masters of the Body—Endocrines

Part of the heavy traffic of food and oxygen racing along the highways of the bloodstream to the body cells is a flow of special messengers. These messengers, called hormones, are fluids made in the body's glands. There are several kinds of hormones, and each kind comes from a special part of the body.

Most glands are tiny sacs or tubes that manufacture special fluids. Sweat glands, tear glands, and salivary glands pour their fluids through tiny hollow pipes called ducts. The glands that make hormones are different from any of these. They pour their fluids directly into the bloodstream. For this reason they are called the ductless glands. They are scattered throughout the body and they make up a special control system—the endocrine system.

Before the twentieth century, nothing was known about the endocrine system. Today we know that if some of these glands are removed or damaged, the body may cease to live within a very few days. How fast we grow, how strong we are, where we get the strength to fight when angry, and how well the cells change food into energy—

all depend on the hormones of our endocrine system. The hormones are the masters of the body.

In an army, officers are in charge of the soldiers. But every officer has a still higher officer whom he must obey—all the way up to the commander-in-chief. In the body, the various glands control the way certain systems work, and the glands themselves are under still other masters.

The commander-in-chief of the ductless glands is a gland less than half an inch across. It is set in a bony hollow in the skull at the base of the brain. The front and back parts of this gland, the pituitary, are really two separate glands that are very close together.

The front part manufactures at least six different hormones. Five of these are special messengers that control other ductless glands, making this part of the pituitary the master gland of the entire system. The sixth hormone goes directly to the billions of body cells and directly controls their growth. It is called the growth hormone. When the pituitary sends out too much of this hormone, the body can grow to unusual size, particularly if the person is young. In full-grown people, when too much growth hormone is sent into the blood-stream the bones do not grow longer. Instead, the face, hands, and feet enlarge. Some tissues also swell.

The rear portion of the pituitary is very different from its immediate neighbor. One of its hormones increases the blood pressure. It also tightens the muscles of the intestine, and decreases the secretion of urine.

One of the hormones from the front part of the pituitary is known by its initials—ACTH; it is a special messenger controlling another ductless gland that sends out its own hormones. ACTH passes through the bloodstream to two small organs, one on top of each kidney. These are the adrenal glands.

Each adrenal gland is divided into an outer part, or cortex, and an inner part, or medulla. Each part secretes different hormones.

The hormones of the cortex regulate the use and storage of protein, fat, and carbohydrate. They control the amount of water the body retains or excretes. They watch over the important salts of the body and influence growth and development. They have other effects on blood-forming tissues and on the color of the skin. Altogether they are so important that until doctors learned to isolate and duplicate these hormones, life was impossible if the adrenal glands were removed or became severely diseased.

The medulla secretes two hormones, of which the better known is adrenaline. Though not essential to life, this hormone regulates some very important functions. It raises the blood pressure, increases the heart's activity and body temperature, and makes more sugar immediately available for use. In an emergency, the adrenal medulla prepares the body for flight or fight, depending upon what the brain decides to do. Although the medulla is not so vital to life as the cortex, the body would not be able to meet sudden crises as well without it. The other hormone of the medulla, called noradrenaline, is similar in structure and action to adrenaline.

The pituitary gland is the commander-in-chief of the other ductless glands, controlling their activity. In addition, the front of the gland controls body growth and sex characteristics. The back controls the artery muscles and the absorption of liquid from the kidneys into the blood.

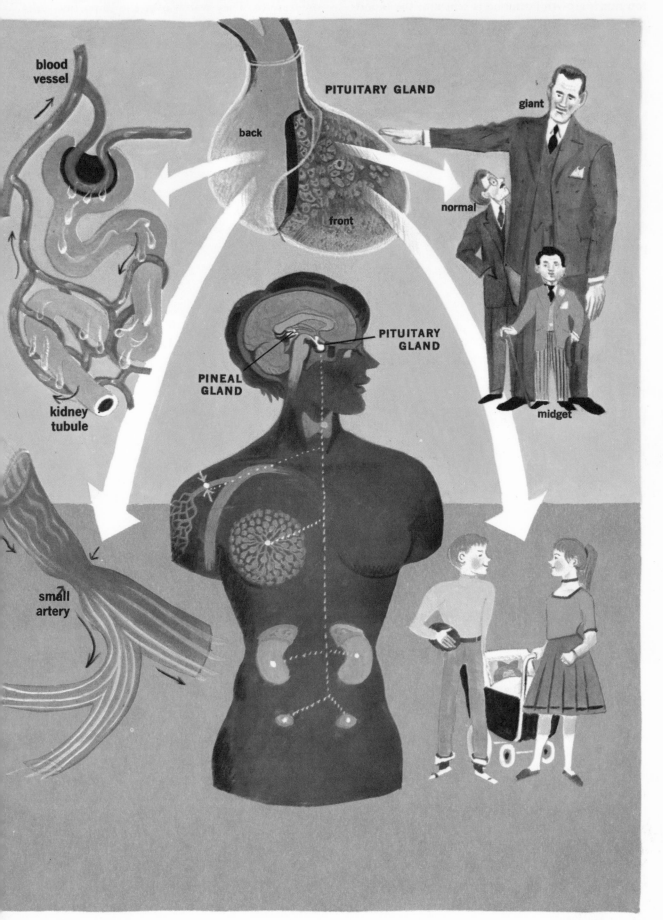

blood
vessel

PITUITARY GLAND

giant

back

normal

front

kidney
tubule

PITUITARY
GLAND

PINEAL
GLAND

midget

small
artery

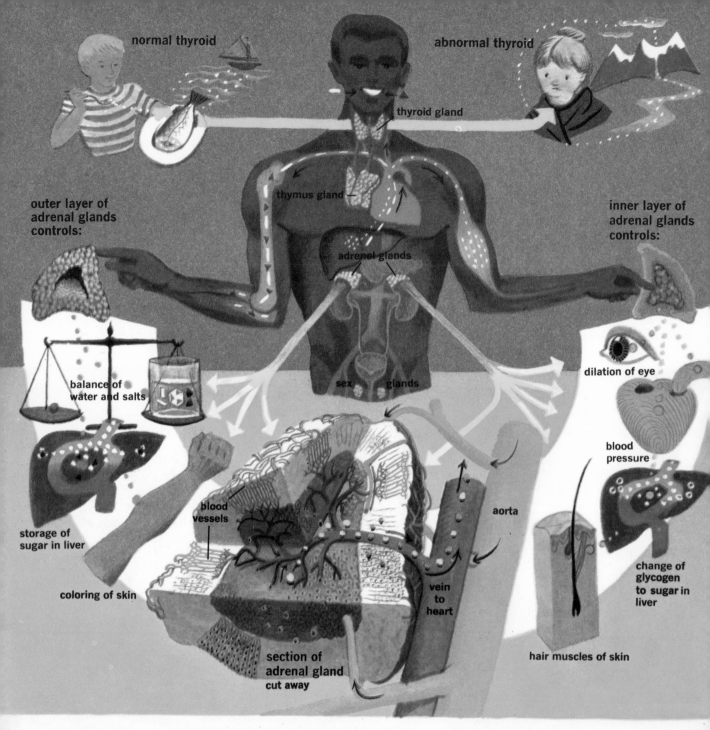

normal thyroid

abnormal thyroid

thyroid gland

thymus gland —

outer layer of adrenal glands controls:

inner layer of adrenal glands controls:

adrenal glands

balance of water and salts

dilation of eye

storage of sugar in liver

blood vessels

sex glands

blood pressure

coloring of skin

aorta

change of glycogen to sugar in liver

vein to heart

section of adrenal gland cut away

hair muscles of skin

The thyroid, adrenal, and thymus glands are all ductless glands. The functions and the complicated structure of the adrenal glands are shown above. In infancy, the thymus manufactures blood cells; its later functions are unknown. The thyroid may swell if iodine is lacking in the diet.

One of the hormones from the front part of the pituitary gland controls the activity of an H-shaped gland that lies at the front of the neck and extends downward from the lower part of the Adam's apple. This gland, the thyroid, secretes a hormone that helps control the speed at which body cells work. If the thyroid is removed or fails to develop, the person is sluggish and may be both physically and mentally retarded.

The thyroid hormone contains iodine. When not enough iodine is taken into the body, all the cells work harder and produce thyroid swelling. This was once common in places where iodine was lacking in food. Now iodine is added to table salt, and the condition is unusual.

Behind the thyroid are four very much smaller glands, the parathyroids. They control the speed at which calcium is taken from the bones and deposited in the bloodstream, where it is important to the proper functioning of the nervous system.

Another hormone center directly controls the body's ability to use sugar. This center is composed of islands of tissue, called the islands of Langerhans, in the pancreas. Most of the pancreas is devoted to making digestive fluids. But the hormone-producing islands are no more a part of the digestive system than the inner ear—which keeps the body balanced—is related to hearing. The hormone from the pancreas, like all hormones, passes directly into the bloodstream.

Since this hormone is manufactured in islands in the pancreas, it is called insulin, from the Latin word *insula*, "an island." It passes through the bloodstream to the liver and muscles and allows them to take sugar from the blood and store it away in the form known as glycogen. Great amounts of sugar form in the blood and urine. This is because the body, if it lacks sufficient insulin, cannot store sugar. The result is the disease known as diabetes. Mild cases can be controlled by a properly regulated diet, but severe cases need special treatment.

The parathyroid glands lie behind the thyroid. Their hormones control the balance of calcium and phos-phorus between the blood and bones. The islands of Langerhans in the pancreas produce the hormone called insulin. The pancreas also supplies digestive juices to the small intestine.

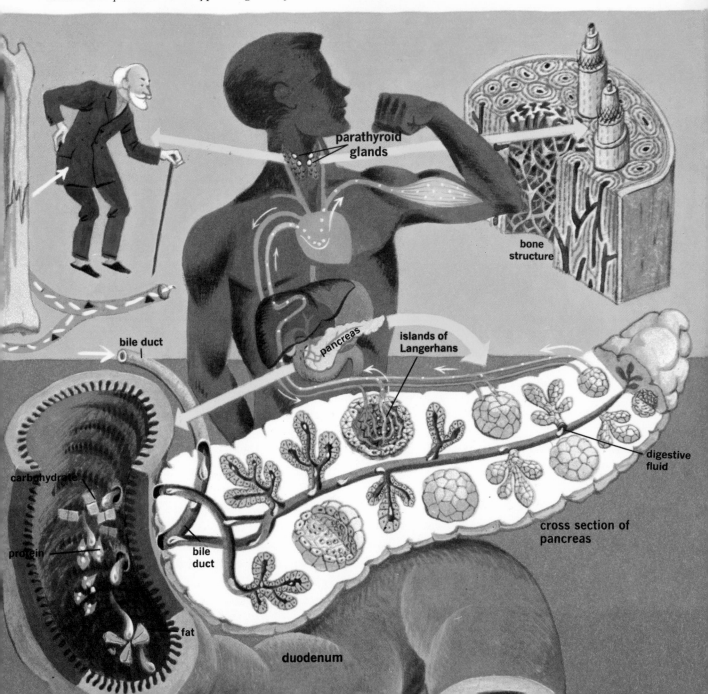

The One Immortal Cell

side view of
sperm cell
magnified

front view of
sperm cell
magnified

sperm

ovum

sperm cell fertilizes ovum

$\mathbf{A}$LL DAY long, every day of the year, every year we live, some of the tissues of our bodies are reproducing themselves. The cells of these tissues create new cells just like themselves by dividing in two. Skin is constantly renewed because its outer layers are continuously being rubbed off. Cartilage, bone, and involuntary muscle also can reproduce themselves when they are injured and new tissue is required. Some of our tissues, such as heart muscle and the cells of the central nervous system, cannot reproduce themselves. But reproduction is the ordinary everyday work of many of the cells of the body.

There is one kind of reproduction that is even more remarkable than cell reproduction. This is the reproduction of the entire living body.

One of the most important differences between tissue reproduction and life reproduction is that life reproduction cannot normally start from a single cell. It starts instead from a combination of two cells which are different in shape, size, and—most particularly—origin. One comes from the male body; the other is made within the female.

The female cell, or ovum (the Latin word for egg), is produced about every twenty-eight days within the female body. It is about the size of a pinpoint, and disappears within a few days unless it is joined by a male cell.

The male cells also have an ancient name—sperm, from the Greek word for seed. The sperm cells are different from every other cell in the body. They are the only cells that can propel themselves about. Sperm cells are many times smaller than

A child's sex is determined by chromosomes that are transmitted by the parents. There are two types of these sex-determining chromosomes, called X and Y chromosomes. Women have only the X chromosomes; men have both X and Y. A child who receives two X-type chromosomes becomes a girl. One who receives an X and a Y becomes a boy. Chromosomes are carried by ovum and sperm cells. When a sperm enters an ovum, the ovum is fertilized. Only a fertilized ovum can grow into a human being.

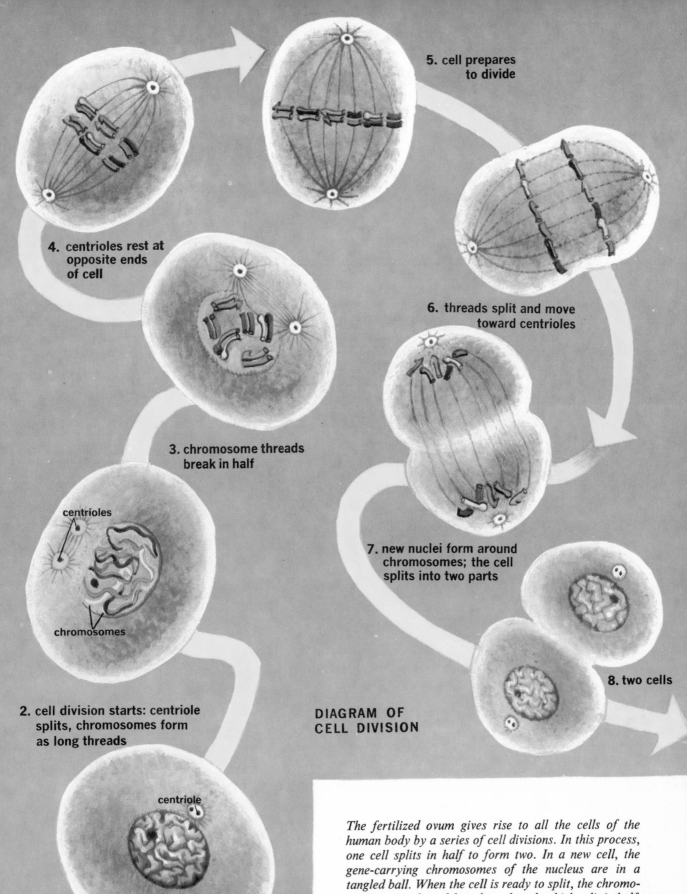

5. cell prepares
   to divide

4. centrioles rest at
   opposite ends
   of cell

6. threads split and move
   toward centrioles

3. chromosome threads
   break in half

centrioles

chromosomes

7. new nuclei form around
   chromosomes; the cell
   splits into two parts

8. two cells

2. cell division starts: centriole
   splits, chromosomes form
   as long threads

DIAGRAM OF
CELL DIVISION

centriole

1. fertilized cell

The fertilized ovum gives rise to all the cells of the
human body by a series of cell divisions. In this process,
one cell splits in half to form two. In a new cell, the
gene-carrying chromosomes of the nucleus are in a
tangled ball. When the cell is ready to split, the chromosomes untangle and form long threads which split in half.
The halves move to opposite ends of the cell and new
nuclei form. The cell splits and two cells, each with the
same number of chromosomes as the original, are
formed.

125

egg cells, and most of the sperm cell's size is taken up by its long tail which can whip back and forth and thereby move the cell forward. The most important part of the sperm cell is the forward part, or head, which is oval in shape. Sperms can be seen only under a microscope. For every ovum, there are millions of sperm cells produced.

If sperm cells are present in the female body during the few days of an ovum's existence, one of the millions of fast-moving cells is likely to come in contact with the ovum. When this happens, the sperm enters the ovum. This is how a human being begins.

Even though the sperm and ovum look different, each contains a twisted pack of separate thread-like chains of beads, or genes. The chains are called chromosomes.

The special cells that are responsible for reproduction do not develop in the same way as do the body cells. Cells generally have a fixed number of chromosomes, but the sperm and ovum each have only half the normal number. When the nuclei of the sperm and ovum come together, the combined cell thus has the full amount.

The cells that will become a new human being continue to multiply rapidly, forming a cluster of small cells.

In the combined cell, the long, threadlike chromosomes split lengthwise, half the threads going to one end of the cell, the other half to the other end. The cell itself then splits, each part taking half of the threads. The threads are by this time so tangled together that each part of the new cell has some from the sperm and some from the ovum. The genes that the sperm chromosomes carry are those that give the offspring the characteristics of the father. Those from the ovum give the characteristics of the mother.

All this has gone on very rapidly, for from the time the sperm first entered the ovum until the combined cell begins to split, only about a day has passed.

Once the splitting begins, it goes on continually, and a cluster of cells is formed. On the seventh day, the growing cluster of cells attaches itself to the inner wall of the part of the mother's body called the uterus. The cluster of cells is eventually fed by blood passing through this point of attachment. Within a few weeks, blood vessels form. As the cell cluster continues to increase, its center becomes hollow.

This cluster is no larger than the original ovum. But soon the size increases and three layers of tissue are

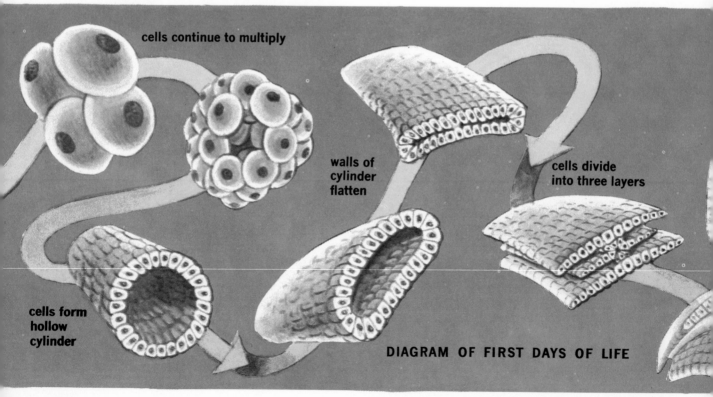

cells continue to multiply

walls of cylinder flatten

cells divide into three layers

cells form hollow cylinder

DIAGRAM OF FIRST DAYS OF LIFE

Gradually the cells arrange themselves in layers as they multiply. The outer layer will develop into the skin and its attachments, into part of the eye and ear, and also into the nervous system including the brain and spinal cord. The middle layer produces the muscles, kidneys, skeleton, heart, and blood vessels. The inner layer produces the digestive system, part of the ear, the lungs, some of the glands, and the bladder. By the fourth week the embryo, as the developing being is called, has begun to take on a form resembling, although distantly, the baby that will be born some eight months later.

All through this change and growth, a part of the body is developing which will, when the time comes, be able to produce new sperm or egg cells— so that the cells of life never really die.

Babies are born with the organs to produce reproductive cells, but the organs are inactive. When a child reaches the early teens, his or her body begins to show changes. A girl develops a figure; a boy's voice begins to crack and squeak and he looks hopefully in the mirror for the first sign of a beard.

formed. These are called germ layers, and from these layers come all the body organs.

These and other alterations indicate the early beginnings of growing up. The organs that produce the reproductive cells are also developing so that when a young man and woman mature, they are able to have babies just as their parents did before them, and their children will after them.

About nine months are needed to produce the human baby. Different animals have their young in widely varying periods of time. Horses take over a year to have colts. Cows produce calves in about the same time as human beings produce their young. Rabbits can have up to four sets of young a year.

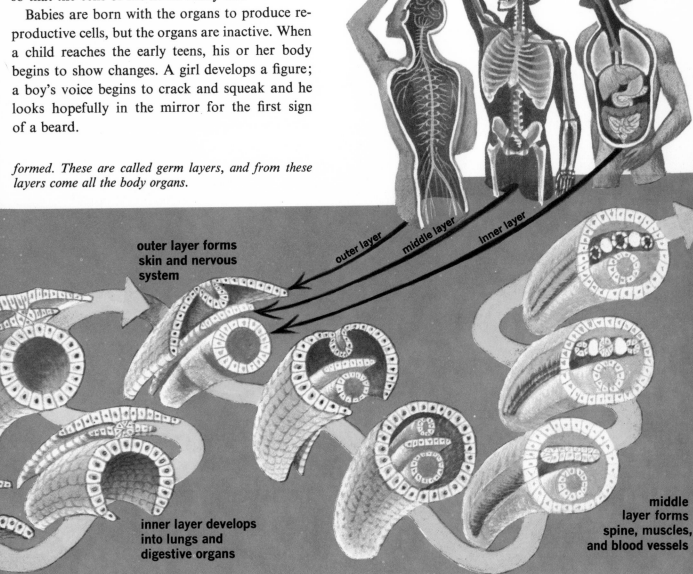

outer layer   middle layer   inner layer

outer layer forms skin and nervous system

inner layer develops into lungs and digestive organs

middle layer forms spine, muscles, and blood vessels

Start of a New Life

Have you ever seen an explosion? It happens so quickly that unless you are looking in the right direction, you will miss it altogether. A movie that makes everything look slowed up shows that most of the explosion takes place at the very beginning, and then gradually eases up as it goes along. The growth and development of the human body is very much like an explosion that takes place over 70 or 80 years—most of the change and growth takes place at the very beginning.

An infant grows from about two feet long to around five to six feet in sixteen years or so. In other words, the body grows to about three times its original length. But before it reaches the outside world it grows from a single tiny cell into an infant ready to be born. After the sperm joins the ovum, the combined cell increases its size more than 3000 times in nine months!

Wonderful changes and growth take place before the infant is born. At no time afterward does it grow and change so much and so fast.

By the end of only three weeks, the single cell has grown into a many-celled being with a rounded shape and an extension of the body where the

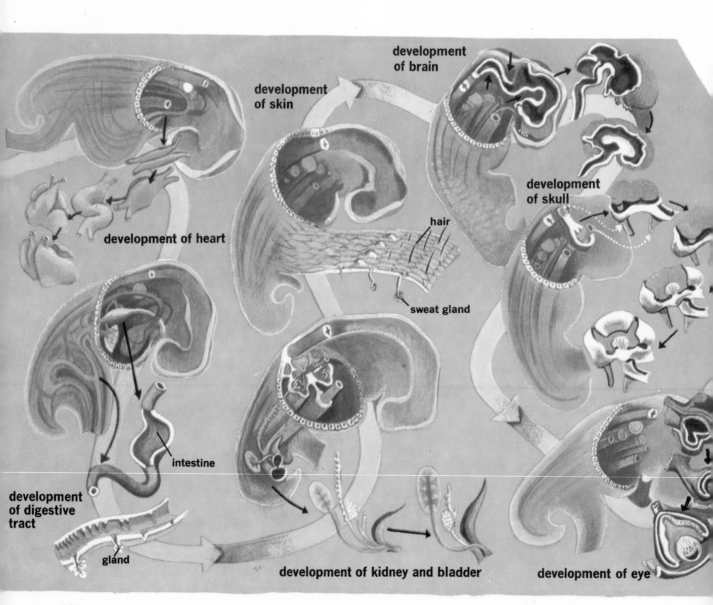

development of brain

development of skin

development of skull

hair

sweat gland

development of heart

intestine

development of digestive tract

gland

development of kidney and bladder

development of eye

Embryos of many different kinds of animals look very much alike in the early stages of development.

heart is already forming. Days pass, and growth and change are ceaseless. Little buds appear which will grow to become arms and legs. The eyes begin to develop, and then the ears. The extension grows beyond the budding heart and gradually enlarges to become a little chest and an abdomen.

By the end of seven weeks, the original cell has become a being that is close to a hundred times as large as it was in the beginning—almost three-quarters of an inch long. A Greek word, *embryo*, is the name for what will eventually become a living human being. In the human embryo about two months old, a human form can already be recognized. The head is not so bent over as it was before and the body is straightened. Eyelids, nose, lips, ears, and cheeks can all be seen. The limb buds have taken on the appearance of arms and legs, and the thumbs are well marked off from the other fingers.

Between the third and fourth month, the size of the embryo doubles. The muscles have become active. The heartbeat is strong, having started about the fourth week. At the end of about an-

The pictures on the preceding pages showed the step-by-step development of body cells and tissues. The developments shown below and at left are not in sequence—they all take place at about the same time. Most body organs are recognizable after about three months.

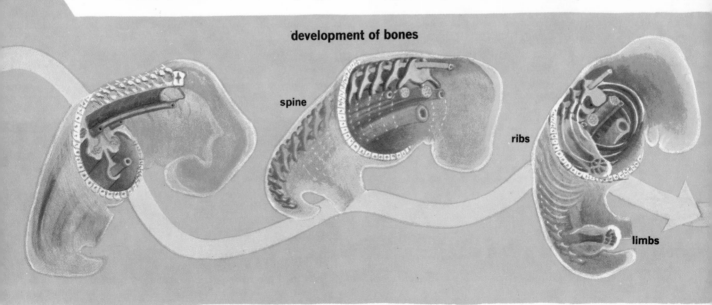

development of bones

spine

ribs

limbs

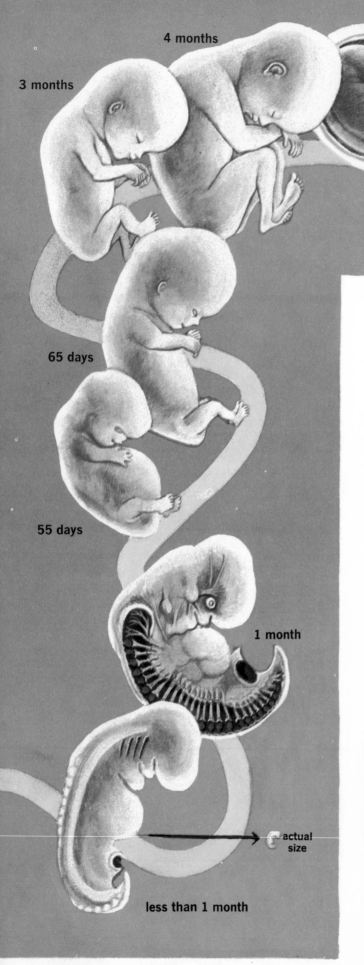

3 months

4 months

ready for birth

at birth

65 days

55 days

1 month

actual size

less than 1 month

other month, little toenails and fingernails have come into being. There is also the beginning of hair on the head.

For all the rapid growth in length and weight, many of the parts of the body necessary to life—such as those for breathing and digestion—are still not developed. They are still not ready to work even six months after the sperm and the ovum came together. The embryo's bloodstream is nourished by that of the mother through a special structure called the placenta, which is attached to the mother's uterus. The cells of the child's growing body are nourished indirectly by the same red blood cells and plasma that feed the cells of the mother's body. The blood vessels that connect the placenta to the child are twisted into a cord. This

After the first three months or so, the human embryo is a human being in miniature. From then until birth, the embryo grows larger and gains weight and strength, preparing for birth.

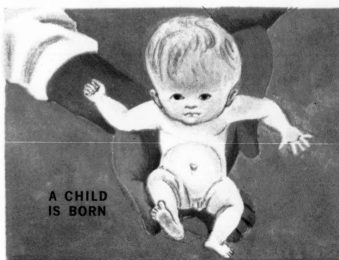

A CHILD IS BORN

cord is cut at birth by the doctor, leaving only the navel.

One month before the child is born, it weighs a few pounds and is around fifteen inches long. Whether it is to be a boy or girl has been clear for about five months now—ever since the end of the fourth month. The bones of the head are soft and flexible, but if the baby were to be born at this time, it would easily be able to stay alive.

The last month before birth is the time given to strengthening a baby for life in the outside world. The length does not change very much but the weight increases greatly. The skin smooths out. The internal organs—circulation of blood, breathing, and digestion—are now fully developed.

At the time when the baby is finally ready to be born, he or she is about nineteen inches in length and weighs, on the average, about seven pounds. The skin is firm, and is pink and smooth. The fingernails are also firm and have grown the full distance down to the tips of the fingers. The ears stand well out from the head, the bones of the head are fairly hard, the voice is loud and strong.

Now the infant is ready for the glorious adventure of life in the outside world, to be greeted with love by the family, to grow, to learn the wonders that wait to be discovered.

A newborn baby's bones are formed largely of tough, rubbery cartilage. This is gradually changed into bone. In some bones, the bone forms in the middle and at each end. Meanwhile, the cartilage in between grows, lengthening the bone. As some cells form bone, others destroy it (below, left). In this way a bone is molded into proper form as it grows. Body proportions (below, right) are determined by bone growth. In a young baby, the head is considerably larger, in proportion to the body, than it is in an adult.

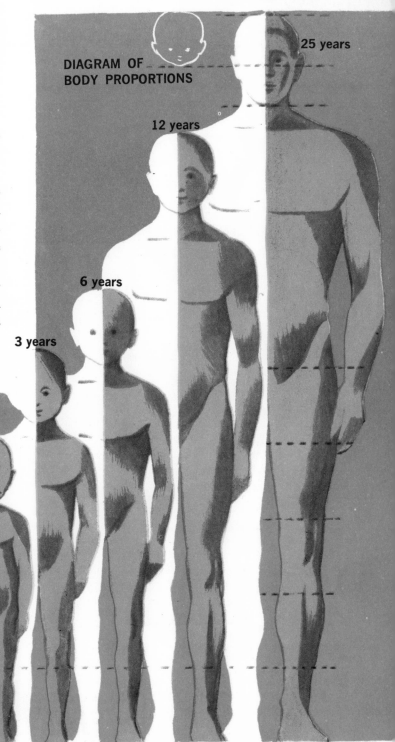

DIAGRAM OF BODY PROPORTIONS

25 years

12 years

6 years

3 years

1 year

at birth

HOW BONES GROW

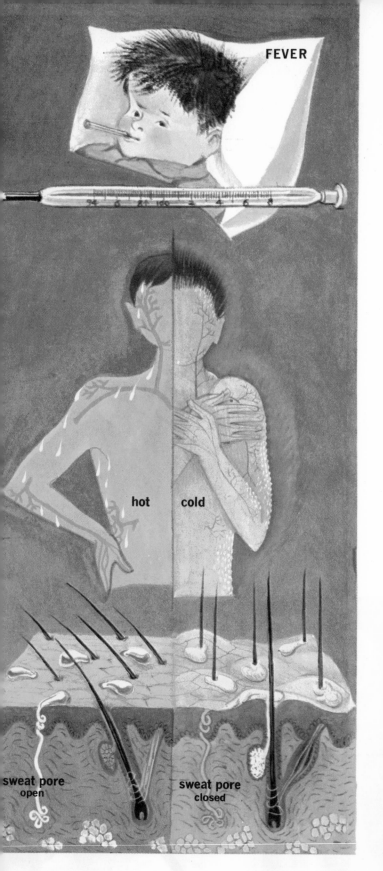

When the body is hot, the blood vessels just below the skin expand, the sweat pores open and give off fluid, and the body is cooled by the evaporation of the fluid. When the body is cold, the blood vessels become narrow, blood is kept deep inside the body, and the sweat pores close. Sometimes tiny bumps, or goose pimples, form.

What Fever Is

ONE morning you may have awakened feeling rather strange. When you stood up, you felt dizzy and tired. You felt as if you ached all over. You were told to stay in bed and the thermometer was put into your mouth. After wrestling it with your tongue for a moment, you settled down and listened to the clock tick off a minute or two. The thermometer was then taken out and read. You were told you had a fever.

What *is* fever? What was going on inside your body?

Suppose you have an empty can with a hole in the bottom and you pour water into it faster than it runs out. In a very short time the can will fill, then overflow. If, on the other hand, you pour water into it just as fast as it runs out, the level of water in the can will not change. In the same way, when the body develops heat faster than the body can cool off, the body gets hotter than it normally is. When this happens, we are said to be running a fever.

The body gets rid of heat through the skin. A fine network of tiny blood vessels carries the blood just beneath the outer surface of the skin, which is cooled by the air. When the surface of the skin gets hot because the blood is heated by exertion, sunlight, or hot air, special skin glands give out a fluid that evaporates, taking heat with it. This cooling process is called sweating.

The body temperature of a healthy person stays about the same in cold weather and warm. On a hot day, the blood vessels just below the skin expand, allowing more blood to be brought to the surface to be cooled. In cool weather the blood vessels become narrow, keeping more blood deep inside the body and so avoiding heat loss.

When the skin pores—the openings of the sweat glands—remain closed, the body cannot get rid of heat. Usually the thermometer reads around 98.6 degrees for the body temperature. You know you have a fever when the thermometer reads a higher temperature. Of course, the normal body temperature does not remain absolutely constant at all times. What the body is doing can affect the temperature. Immediately after you have been running very hard, for example, the thermometer might read 100 degrees for a brief time. Real fever generally begins around 101 degrees, although there are many cases of lower fevers accompanying illness.

Fever itself is not a sickness—it is a sign that the body is fighting off infection. Fever occurs with a great many different kinds of disease.

Some doctors and scientists believe that the body raises its own temperature to defend itself against infection. This is the way they explain what is happening:

When the brain receives the message that foreign bodies, such as bacteria, have invaded the system, the sweat glands are closed off and the tiny blood vessels near the surface of the skin are contracted. This does two things. First, more blood is sent to the interior of the body, bringing a large number of white cells to fight the infection; second, the temperature of the body is raised. This increase in heat kills many enemy bacteria.

Sometimes the fever is not spread throughout the body, as with an infectious disease. In the case of an infected cut, for example, blood seeping into the cut acts like a foreign substance, and the flesh around the infection is hot and feverish to the touch—yet a thermometer placed in the mouth would show a normal body temperature.

Fevers sometimes come and go in patterns, depending on the particular infection. In some cases the temperature rises and falls to normal every day during the course of an attack; in other cases the temperature makes smaller swings every day without settling at normal; and in still others attacks of fever come at intervals several days apart. Doctors get information about the disease from which a patient is suffering from the pattern in which the fever climbs and falls.

A fever is not in itself necessarily serious unless the temperature rises to around 105 degrees. Fever is a sign that the body is making a special effort to remain well.

Doctors knew about fever long before they knew about thermometers. Over five thousand years ago, Egyptian doctors wrote about fevers they had detected with the oldest instrument a doctor has—his hands.

Fever increases the activity of all the body's organs. The number of white cells increases and the cells move through the body destroying foreign particles. After fever, the sweat glands release their fluid, the skin's pores open, and the excess heat is lost through perspiration.

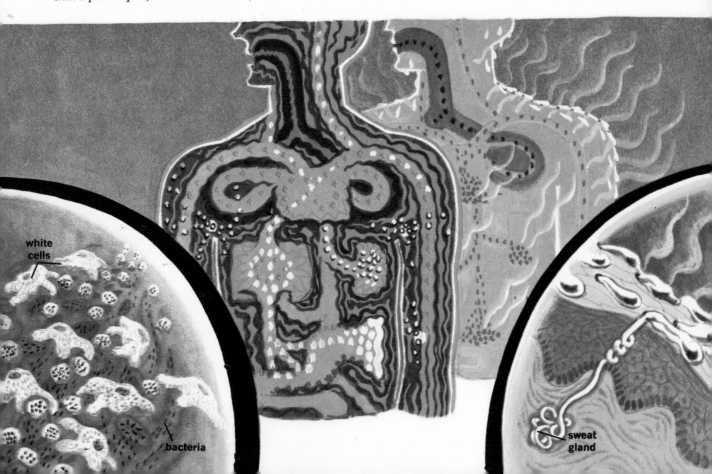

BACTERIAL GROWTH

Not all bacteria are harmful. Some are useful. They aid in making cheese, wine, vinegar, and dough for bread. The reproductive power of all bacteria is astounding. When a farmer pours milk into a can, there may be thousands of bacteria in the can. If unchecked, they can multiply at such a fantastic rate that in the course of a day they may increase to millions.

Keeping Healthy

THROUGHOUT recorded history, doctors and other medical men have devoted enormous amounts of energy to finding ways of treating disease and making the sick well. In ancient times, and even to some extent until quite recently, great epidemics spread over parts of the world, causing untold death and disease. Such epidemics are rare nowadays, and those that occur are less violent. One reason is the discovery of antibiotics. But this is only part of the answer. Of far greater importance is our increased knowledge of measures to prevent illness, rather than simply to cure it. Such measures are called preventive medicine.

In general, there are four different ways by which we keep our bodies healthy. These are personal hygiene, general public health measures, injections to prevent specific diseases, and first-aid measures.

Personal hygiene includes the steps all of us take to keep ourselves healthy. It does not concern the doctor, except that he might remind us of steps we neglect. Personal hygiene includes washing the hands to avoid picking up germs, brushing bacteria and particles of food from the teeth to keep from developing cavities, and bathing to remove possibly dangerous bacteria from the skin. Getting enough sleep is also a matter of personal hygiene. The body, and especially a growing body, resists disease and infection far better if it is well rested. A tired body is more receptive to germs.

Public health measures are the steps taken by a community to protect the health of the community's individual citizens. In a city or town, the water supply is controlled by a public health

134

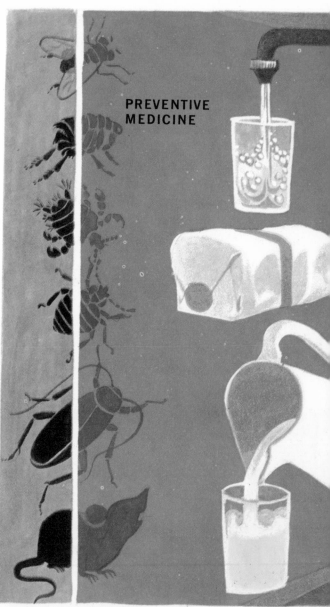

PREVENTIVE MEDICINE

When the body is invaded by certain types of foreign matter called antigens, it produces antibodies which counteract the antigens and keep them from doing harm

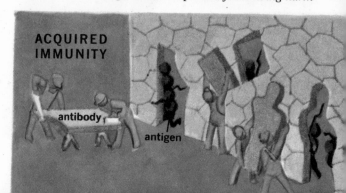

ACQUIRED IMMUNITY

antibody

antigen

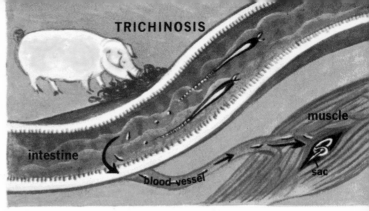

TRICHINOSIS

muscle

intestine

blood vessel

sac

Some diseases can be prevented in the home. One of these is trichinosis. This is caused by a worm that is sometimes found in undercooked pork. When the pork is eaten, the worm is carried from the intestine to a muscle. There it forms a small sac or capsule in which it coils up. Trichinosis can be very painful, but if pork is sufficiently cooked, it can be avoided.

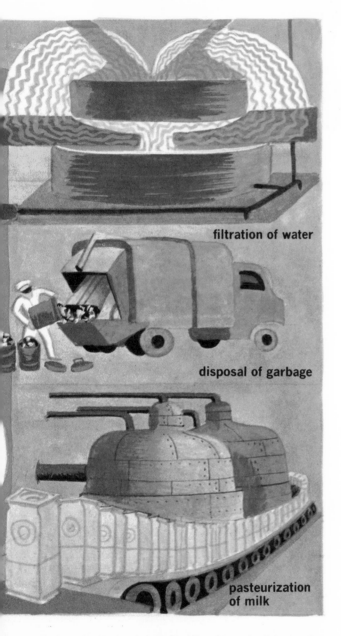

filtration of water

disposal of garbage

pasteurization of milk

to the body. This is an example of acquired immunity. Antigens may also be inoculated into the body in small doses. This brings about passive immunity.

IMMUNITY BY INOCULATION

officer or a department of water supply. These officers are either doctors or are supervised by doctors. They make sure that the source of the water is clean, and that the pipes are in good condition. If there are impurities in the water, the officials see that it is filtered, or that purifying chemicals are added. These men also inspect cows, barns, and dairies to make sure that milk is pure and free from disease-bearing bacteria.

Other important public health measures include controlling insects that carry certain diseases, and preventing factories from polluting the air with smoke and harmful gases.

Injections to prevent disease are the special responsibility of the doctor. About two hundred years ago, it was discovered that one of the most terrible and feared diseases—smallpox—could be prevented by scratching the skin and allowing a special substance called vaccine to seep into the bloodstream. This procedure was named vaccination. Doctors have since found out that many other serious diseases including diphtheria, infantile paralysis (or polio), and tetanus can be prevented by the proper injections.

The fourth measure for staying healthy is first aid. This is a way of preventing an illness or injury from becoming more serious. If a cut is washed out and a dressing put on it, it will probably heal without trouble. If it is left untended, it may become infected. Of course, first-aid measures are really emergency treatments, and if the injury is at all serious, the patient should be taken to a doctor for true medical care.

The doctor, however, should not be consulted only when one is sick. Regular check-ups allow him to examine the body and find any minor ailments or defects that might turn into something more serious.

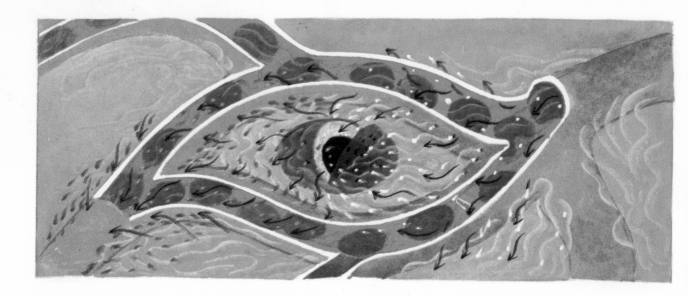

Glossary

ADRENAL GLAND Either of two glands, one on each kidney, that regulate the use of carbohydrates and salt and prepare the body for emergencies.

ALVEOLI Tiny air sacs in the lungs. In them, oxygen enters and carbon dioxide is taken from the bloodstream.

AMINO ACID Any of the nitrogen-containing acids, essential to life, that make up protein.

AMPULLA A saclike swelling, as in the semicircular canals of the inner ear.

ANTIBODY Any of the special substances produced by the blood to combat the harmful effect of a foreign substance.

ANTIGEN Any foreign substance that enters the bloodstream and triggers the production of antibodies.

ANVIL See HAMMER.

AORTA The body's major artery. (See also ARTERY)

APPENDIX A useless fingerlike pouch hanging from one end of the large intestine.

ARTERY Any of the large blood vessels that carry blood from the heart.

ATRIUM Either of the two upper heart chambers. Also called auricle.

AUDITORY TUBE A tube connecting the ear and the back of the nose. Also called Eustachian tube.

AURICLE Either one of the two upper chambers of the heart; also, the outer part of the ear.

AXON A nerve fiber, usually long and slender, that carries impulses away from a nerve cell.

BACTERIA A group of microscopic, one-celled organisms. Some are harmful, others are helpful to man.

BICUSPID Any of eight permanent teeth used for grinding and crushing. There are two on each side of the upper and lower jaws between the molars and the canine teeth. Also called premolars.

BILE A juice made in the liver, stored in the gall bladder, and supplied to the small intestine for use in digestion.

BLADDER A sac that collects urine from the kidney for excretion.

BRAIN A large mass of nerve tissue in the skull where learning and other mental activities take place.

BRONCHI Short tubes that connect the windpipe to the lungs. Also called bronchial tubes.

BURSAE Small sacs, lined with smooth membrane and filled with fluid, that lie around joints and the ends of bones. Bursae cushion shocks between them and muscles.

CALLUS A thick swelling of hardened bone tissue that forms around a bone break; also, an area of thick, hardened skin.

CALORIE A unit of heat used to measure the energy value of food.

CANINE TOOTH Any of the four pointed teeth next to the incisors, so named because they are large in dogs.

CAPILLARY Any of the minute blood vessels that carry blood to the body cells.

CARBOHYDRATE One of the three main classes of food essential to man. Sugar is the most common carbohydrate.

CARPUS The wrist. It is composed of eight small bones.

CARTILAGE A hard, rubbery tissue that covers the ends of bones where they form joints. It is also found in the ears, the tip of the nose, and elsewhere.

CECUM The part of the large intestine that connects with the small intestine.

CELL The smallest unit of life, consisting of a tiny mass of protoplasm enclosed in a membrane. All living things are made up of cells.

CENTRIOLE A small structure in cells that is active in cell division.

CEREBELLUM The lower rear part of the brain. It coordinates the movement of different muscles and helps the body maintain its balance.

CEREBRAL CORTEX The outer tissue of the brain.

CEREBRUM The upper and main part of the brain, where learning takes place.

CHROMOSOME Any of the threadlike bodies in the nucleus of a cell that contain the units of heredity called genes.

CHYME Partly digested food that enters the small intestine from the stomach.

CILIA Small, hairlike projections on certain cells, chiefly in the breathing passages. Cilia wave to and fro, sweeping out dust and other particles.

COCCYX The four lowest vertebrae of the spine. Also called the tailbone.

COCHLEA The spiral-shaped organ of the inner ear; it is here that sounds are converted into nerve impulses, which are sent to the brain.

COLON A section of the large intestine, which passes up one side of the abdominal cavity, crosses to the other side, then leads down.

CONE Any of the many cells in the retina of the eye that distinguish between colors and give sharp focus to vision.

CORNEA The tough, transparent covering of the eyeball that lies over the iris and pupil.

CORTEX The outer part of an organ or structure, as the gray matter forming the outer layer of most of the brain.

CRANIUM The skull.

DELTOID Shaped like the Greek capital letter delta (Δ), as the deltoid muscle of the upper arm.

DENDRITE A short, branching nerve fiber that carries impulses to the body of a nerve cell.

DENTINE The medium-hard inner layer of a tooth.

DERMIS The inner layer of the skin. It contains the skin's blood vessels and nerve endings.

DIAPHRAGM A sheet of muscle dividing the chest from the abdomen. It helps to fill and empty the lungs during breathing.

DUCT A tube or vessel that carries fluid, usually from a gland.

DUCTLESS GLAND See ENDOCRINE GLAND.

DUODENUM The first section of the small intestine, connecting with the stomach.

EMBRYO An unborn child in the early stages of development.

ENAMEL The hard outer layer of a tooth.

ENDOCRINE GLAND Any of certain glands that pour their secretions directly into the bloodstream rather than into ducts. Also called ductless glands.

ENDOLYMPH A fluid in the cochlea of the inner ear.

ENZYME A complex substance that brings about chemical changes in the body, as in digestion.

EPIDERMIS The outer layer of the skin.

EPIGLOTTIS A thin flap of cartilage that closes the entrance to the larynx when food is swallowed.

ESOPHAGUS The tube through which food passes in going from the pharynx, or throat, to the stomach.

EUSTACHIAN TUBE See AUDITORY TUBE.

EXOCRINE GLAND Any of the glands, such as the tear gland of the eye, that send their fluids through ducts.

FALX One of two sickle-shaped membranes that lie between the cerebrum and cerebellum.

FAT One of the three main classes of food essential to man. Fats are the body's chief storage source of energy.

FETUS An unborn child in the later stages of development.

FIBRIN A threadlike protein substance which forms from blood when it clots.

FIBRINOGEN A blood protein converted to fibrin during clotting.

FOLLICLE A simple gland or cavity in the skin from which hair grows.

GALL BLADDER A small sac attached to the liver in which bile is stored.

GALLSTONES Crystals that may form in the gall bladder. Sometimes they block the bile ducts and have to be removed by surgery.

GENE Any of the minute packets of substances in cells that determine what characteristics will be passed on from parents to children.

GENETICS The study of heredity, or how parents pass on such characteristics as color of eyes and hair to their offspring.

GLAND An organ that secretes a substance for the body's use. (See also ENDOCRINE GLAND and EXOCRINE GLAND)

HAMMER, ANVIL, and STIRRUP Three tiny connected bones that carry sound vibrations from the eardrum to the inner ear.

HEART The organ that pumps blood through the body.

HEMOGLOBIN A protein that colors red blood cells and enables them to transport oxygen.

HORMONE Any of certain special substances made in one part of the body and carried by the blood to another part, where they help to regulate body activities.

HUMOR Any fluid of the body. (See also VITREOUS BODY)

ILEOCECAL VALVE The valve between the large and small intestines. It connects the lower end (ileum) of the small intestine with the upper end (cecum) of the large intestine.

ILEUM The part of the small intestine that connects with the large intestine.

INCISOR Any of the eight front teeth (four in the upper jaw, four in the lower) used in biting.

INTESTINE See LARGE INTESTINE and SMALL INTESTINE.

IRIS The colored portion, or diaphragm, of the eye. By changing the size of its center opening, the pupil, it regulates the amount of light entering the eye.

ISLANDS OF LANGERHANS The small glands in the pancreas that manufacture the hormone insulin.

JOINT The connection between two bones.

KIDNEY Either one of a pair of organs that remove waste materials from the blood by excreting urine.

LARGE INTESTINE A tube below the small intestine whose chief function is to remove water from food residues and eliminate waste products.

LARYNX The organ of the voice. It lies in the front of the throat and is seen on the outside as the Adam's apple.

LENS A transparent, bean-shaped structure in the eye that focuses light rays on the retina.

LIGAMENT A tough, fibrous tissue that connects bones at joints.

LIVER A large gland having many functions concerned with the digestion, storage, and conversion of food stuffs and the manufacture of certain blood proteins.

LOBULE A small lobe, or section of an organ or part, such as a liver lobule.

LUNG Either of the two respiratory organs which put oxygen into the blood and take out carbon dioxide.

LYMPH A clear, nearly colorless fluid formed from blood serum when it passes through the capillary walls.

MACROPHAGE A large, wandering white blood cell found in such organs as the spleen. One of its main functions is to engulf foreign particles.

MARROW The soft tissue that lies within most bones. In the marrow of certain bones, blood cells are made.

MEDULLA The inner part of an organ or structure.

MEMBRANE A thin, pliable sheet forming an envelope around a body part or lining a body cavity.

MOLAR Any of twelve back teeth with flattened surfaces for crushing and grinding food.

MUCUS A syrupy fluid that moistens and protects membranes of internal body surfaces, such as the inside of the nose, that are in contact with the outside.

MUSCLE Any of the ropes or sheets of tough tissue that move parts of the body.

NERVE CELL Any of the cells, each consisting of cell body and extending fibers, that carry messages in the body.

NUCLEUS A small body within a cell that controls the cell's activities.

OLFACTORY Relating to the sense of smell.

OPTIC Relating to sight.

ORGAN   A group of different tissues working together to do a special job. The heart, the stomach, and the lungs are organs.

ORGANISM   Any living thing.

OVUM   A female egg cell.

PAPILLAE   Tiny projections, as on the tongue. The taste buds lie within the papillae of the tongue.

PARATHYROID GLAND   Any of four small glands behind the thyroid gland. They regulate the calcium content of the blood.

PANCREAS   A digestive gland that secretes pancreatic juice into the intestine and the hormone insulin into the bloodstream.

PELVIS   The firm girdle of bones at the lower end of the trunk by which the legs are attached to the body; also the upper end of the ureter as it leaves the kidney.

PERILYMPH   A fluid in the cochlea of the inner ear.

PERISTALSIS   The progressive squeezing of the muscles of the intestinal tube, which moves food or fluid along.

PHAGOCYTE   A white blood cell which engulfs foreign particles such as bacteria.

PHARYNX   The upper part of the throat, between the mouth and the esophagus.

PIGMENT   Coloring matter.

PITUITARY GLAND   A pea-sized endocrine gland located at the base of the brain. It regulates activities of other endocrine glands and controls body growth.

PLANKTON   Tiny swimming or floating animal or plant life of the sea.

PLASMA   The fluid part of the blood.

PLATELET   A particle in the blood that aids in clotting.

PONS   A bridge, as in the bridge of nervous tissue that connects parts of the brain.

PREMOLAR   See BICUSPID.

PROTEIN   One of the three main classes of food essential to man. Meat, milk, and eggs are rich in proteins.

PROTHROMBIN   A substance that aids in blood clotting.

PROTOPLASM   The complex substance that makes up living tissue.

PROTOZOON (plural protozoa)   Any one-celled animal.

PULP   The soft, sensitive tissue filling the central part of a tooth.

PUPIL   The adjustable opening in the eye through which light passes.

PYLORUS   The narrow passage at the lower end of the stomach connecting with the duodenum, or upper part of the small intestine.

RED BLOOD CELL   Any of the cells that give blood its color and transport oxygen.

REFLEX   An automatic movement or activity in response to a stimulus, as when we pull our hand away after touching something hot.

RETINA   The light-sensitive tissue at the back of the eye.

ROD   Any of the cells in the retina that distinguish between light and dark and enable us to see in dim light.

SAC   A baglike body part, as the air sacs of the lungs.

SACCULE   A small sac in the inner ear.

SACRUM   The part of the backbone that joins with the pelvis.

SALIVARY GLAND   Any of the glands that secrete saliva into the mouth. Saliva begins the breakdown of food and helps it move down the throat.

SEBACEOUS   Like or related to fatty matter, as the sebaceous glands of the skin, which secrete fatty matter.

SEMICIRCULAR CANAL   Any of three loop-shaped tubes in the inner ear that help the body maintain balance.

SERUM   The liquid left after blood clots.

SINUS   A cavity or hollow. The sinuses of the nose are air-filled cavities in the skull that open into the nose.

SMALL INTESTINE   A long tube extending from the stomach to the colon which is the main site of the digestion and absorption of food.

SPERM   A male reproductive cell.

SPINAL CORD   A cord of nerve tissue extending from the brain down the back in the spinal column. It sends messages to and from the brain and controls reflex actions.

SPLEEN   A small organ near the stomach which makes certain white blood cells, destroys worn-out red blood cells, and stores blood.

STIRRUP   See HAMMER.

STOMACH   The muscular pouch in which the early phases of digestion take place.

SYSTEM   All of the organs involved in an important body process, such as digestion.

TAILBONE   See COCCYX.

TARSUS   Seven bones in the arch of the foot. They correspond to the wrist, or carpus, of the hand.

TENDON   A tough, non-stretchable cord of tissue connecting a muscle to a bone.

THROMBOPLASTIN   A substance that aids in blood clotting.

THYMUS   A gland of the lower neck and upper chest, large in infants but shrunken to a mere trace in adults.

THYROID GLAND   An H-shaped gland in the front of the neck. It secretes a hormone that helps control the speed at which body cells work.

TISSUE   A group of similar specialized cells that form a body structure. Skin, muscle, and bone are tissues.

TRACHEA   The main tube through which air passes to and from the lungs. Also called the windpipe.

TUBULE   A small body tube.

URETER   Either of two long tubes, each of which carries liquid wastes from one of the kidneys to the bladder.

URETHRA   A tube that carries urine from the bladder to the outside of the body.

UTRICLE   A small sac in the inner ear.

VALVE   A structure that temporarily closes a passage or opening, or permits a fluid to flow in one direction only.

VEIN   Any of the blood vessels that carry blood back to the heart.

VENTRICLE   A cavity or space in an internal organ, such as either one of the two lower chambers of the heart.

VERTEBRA (plural: vertebrae)   Any of thirty-three separate bones that make up the backbone.

VESSEL   A tube or canal through which a fluid moves, such as a blood vessel.

VILLUS (plural: villi)   One of millions of tiny hairlike projections, as those in the small intestine that help absorb food.

VITAMIN   Any of a number of substances in food that are essential to life. Only minute quantities are needed by the body.

VITREOUS BODY (or HUMOR)   The transparent syrupy fluid that fills the main chamber of the eye.

WHITE BLOOD CELL   Any of the colorless cells that protect the body against disease. Most of them move about freely in the bloodstream.

WINDPIPE   See TRACHEA.

INDEX

Page numbers in *italics* refer to illustrations.

LM

LEEUWENHOEK 1632-1723
first observed living cells

HIPPOCRATES 460-377 B.C.
"the father of medicine"

VESALIUS 1514-1564
explored human anatomy

FABRICIUS 1537-1619
discovered valves of
blood vessels

HARVEY 1578-1657
described circulation of blood

LAVOISIER 1743-1794
discovered body's use of oxygen

BERNARD 1813-1878
demonstrated function of liver